The Little Book of Breathwork

Catherine Carrigan

Book design by RamaJon
Cover design by RamaJon

Available for order through Ingram Press Catalogues

Catherine Carrigan

Visit my websites at

www.catherinecarrigan.com
www.unlimitedenergynow.com

Printed in the United States of America

First Printing: April 2019

ISBN:978-0-9894506-4-5

TABLE OF CONTENTS

BOOK IV
16 SIMPLE MUDRAS TO ACTIVATE DIVINE ENERGY

BOOK I

How I Learned to Breathe Properly

Chapter 1:
My History of Asthma

"As long as there is breath in the body, there is life. When breath departs, so does life. Therefore, regulate the breath."
- Nath Yogi Swatmarama

When I was about 30 years old, I noticed I would get out of breath walking across a flat parking lot.

I went to a medical doctor who diagnosed me with asthma. At the time, he also tested me for environmental allergies.

"I'm going to put you in my allergy hall of fame," the doctor told me.

Apparently, I was allergic -- and not just mildly allergic, but highly reactive -- to every substance he tested me for.

And so began my history of having trouble breathing, using various inhalers as I wheezed and going to the doctor twice a week to receive a series of allergy shots.

I didn't like the inhalers because they made

me feel like not just any old space cadet but a super-spacey space cadet.

Nevertheless, I also didn't like not being able to take a full breath, so I did as I was told.

About the same time, being a reasonable person, I decided for myself that maybe it would be a good idea to start exercising.

Nobody told me to exercise. I just figured it out for myself.

Look at it this way: If I had an asthma attack with my reduced lung capacity, becoming more physically fit meant that maybe, just maybe, my breathing difficulties wouldn't be so scary.

So I joined the local YMCA. I attended aerobics classes, had a little card that allowed me to work the weight machines in the gym and sometimes went swimming after work.

Eventually I disliked the inhalers so much that I simply stopped using them.

I kept having to get allergy shots for a period of about five years.

As I became more fit, I felt better and better about myself even though nobody was teaching me how to breathe properly and I still struggled sometimes.

Three Part Breathing

Chapter 2: Learning to Breathe

"Now is where love breathes."
- *Rumi*

One year when I was still in my early 30s, I went on vacation to Los Angeles. As was and still is my custom, I had come to enjoy taking long walks.

While on vacation, I kept wandering around the city one day until I eventually ended up in front of a yoga studio. A few years earlier, a friend had recommended I take up yoga, but I recall arrogantly replying, "Yoga is for wimps," and quickly dismissed him.

Since I was going to be in L.A. and away from work for more than a week, however, I decided I might as well give this thing a try.

I don't remember much about those first yoga classes other than I felt really good while practicing. There was no huffing and puffing like in the aerobics classes at the YMCA and no straining as there had been in the weight room.

I noticed I could breathe better during the yoga classes than in the highly chlorinated swimming pool. At the time, I didn't think the classes were easy, but then again I really didn't know what I was doing.

At the end of the week, I noticed the studio was selling a videotape for about $10 and decided to make the small investment so I could continue to practice back home in Atlanta.

Little did I realize my entire life was about to change.

I started practicing yoga without a mat on the thick red rug in my living room. Slipping around, I followed the videotaped instructions. I still didn't exactly know what I was doing, but it felt so good I practiced every day for a month.

Although I was just practicing sun salutes, a few standing poses and some backbends, my entire view of spirituality suddenly began to shift.

The church I had patronized no longer felt right for me. Its doctrines rang a little harsh, so I stopped attending.

I can't explain what it was about the yoga exercises on the videotape that changed my viewpoint. All I knew was that the practice gave me a connection to my own soul that I had never experienced before.

I still attend church, but have found a new place to worship that feels kinder and gentler.

At the beginning of the videotape, the beautiful woman instructing the yoga practice guided me to put my hands on my belly to feel myself breathe.

I learned three-part breathing.

You breathe into your belly. Then you keep one hand on your belly and move the other hand to your chest.

Then you move the lower hand up to your ribs and feel them expanding.

You learn to feel yourself breathing three-dimensionally.

For the first time in my life, I became aware of myself breathing.

Even the experience of asthma with all its

restrictions, inhalers and discomfort hadn't connected me back to my breath.

At the end of the video, I was instructed to lie down and relax for five minutes.

That for me was the hardest part of the practice -- lying still and trying to quiet my mind.

Even though I didn't know what I was doing after a month of trying, I felt calmer, more relaxed and happier with myself.

A few months later, I purchased my first yoga mat, and lo and behold, my feet stopped slipping around!

The word "asana" used in yoga translates to "steady and relaxed position." Finally, I was firmly on my feet as I practiced the poses.

I wasn't accustomed to spending money on myself -- first a $10 video and then an actual yoga mat -- so this venture was turning into a major investment.

I had embarked on a journey that to this day still takes me deeper into the steadiest part of myself and makes me aware that I am worth taking care of.

Chapter 3:
Relaxing in a Mental Hospital

"Breathe, darling. This is just a chapter.
It's not your whole story."
- *S.C. Lourie*

Before I was diagnosed with asthma at age 30, I had another brief experience with breathwork although it wasn't described in those terms at the time.

When I was about 20 years old, I suffered a nervous breakdown and was thrown into a mental hospital.

There's not much I can recommend about the experience other than, if it ever happens to you even once, you will resolve to do whatever it takes never to end up in such a place ever again.

At the mental hospital, we had individual and group therapy, and I was prescribed a series of pills.

I felt like an awful person and worried that if I were actually crazy, which is the label they had put on me, then no one might ever love me.

When the doctors finally determined it was safe to let me stroll around the grounds, I took walks in the fresh air whenever possible.

Periodically, our little group got herded into a separate building where we took classes on stress management.

My one positive memory of the place -- aside from the walking -- was lying on the floor of the mental hospital breathing.

We were instructed to tighten and relax our muscles as we visualized a gentle waterfall cascading above the crown of our heads. We were told to breathe into the tight places and imagine ourselves becoming more and more relaxed.

The relaxation flowed through my body as I lay there.

I still didn't realize I was breathing. I just momentarily felt less worried.

It was a different feeling than I had ever had, a calmness I could recreate on my own that did not require popping a pill.

That memory of discovering how to relax for the first time stays with me to this day.

Why hadn't I been taught about the magic and power of breathing on Day One of my visit to the mental hospital?

I just wondered.

Chapter 4: The Hollywood Types Explain It All to Me

"Not everyone was privileged to see another sunrise like you did, so before you start complaining, remember that the breath of life is not for sale."
- Gift Gugu Mona

As I continued practicing yoga at home on my living room rug -- now with my very own brand-new yoga mat -- I enjoyed deepening my breath with three-part breathing.

I felt like a kid with a new toy, so when I rode my bicycle in the Georgia sunshine, I continued breathing as I thought I had learned on the yoga video.

I felt powerful peddling along under the treetops with deep, even breathing, using my full lung capacity. I thought I could ride faster as I practiced my yoga breathing.

But I didn't really learn how to breathe properly until I went back to Los Angeles for another vacation.

I went to another yoga class, this time at a very fancy studio in Hollywood.

I thought I was fitting right in with my loud, sonorous breathing, but then I noticed the other students staring at me. Turns out, they thought I sounded like I was snoring.

"Darth Vadar," one student told me.

I got it!

Instead of snorting, snoring, groaning or making any other loud offensive sound, I was supposed to constrict the back of my throat with my lips closed to do what yogis call Ujayii Breath.

If you've never heard Ujayii Breath but watched the movie *Star Wars*, you will notice Darth Vadar sounds like he's using Ujayii Breath.

Later in this book, I'm going to teach you about Ujayii Breath, which I call Ocean Breath. Essentially, you'll learn to make the sound of the ocean in the back of your throat.

As I continued to study, practice and eventually teach yoga, I learned some schools won’t teach breathwork until a student has been practicing postures for at least a year. I could see why that might be the case.

Most of us carry so much muscular tension that our dome-shaped diaphragm muscle might not be able to expand to its full capacity.

The connective tissue between our ribs and our intercostal muscles (which assist the lungs) can become virtually frozen with trigger points from years of chronic stress.

Practicing yoga releases the general tension in not only your muscles but also the connective tissue called fascia that weaves your body together.

Yoga backbends such as wheel, fish, bridge and cobra can unwind the muscular contractions around your lungs and loosen the connective tissue that has kept you literally physiologically entrapped in your own trauma.

Chapter 5: Video Clips for an Unemployed Barber

"Master your breath, let the self be in bliss, contemplate on the sublime within you."
- Tirumalai Krishnamacharya

As I began teaching yoga, I saw the value of sharing the simplest forms of breathwork with my beginner students so they could discover - just as I had -- the inner peace that has been waiting for them to find through their breath.

As I continued studying yoga, I noticed every time I made a major attempt to deepen my practice, I would unwind another layer of stress.

This deeper and deeper relaxation became its own reward.

I went on to attend not just one but six 200-hour yoga teacher trainings, finally advancing to a 500-hour training before throwing in the towel after two years of studying yoga therapy.

I learned that completing my yoga therapy

degree would not confer the legal right to call myself a yoga therapist or refer to what I did as therapy.

"What's the point?" I thought.

My yoga therapy teacher informed me that getting a degree would require hefty fees and two days of paperwork. I really hate paperwork.

What I had enjoyed most of all during that time was the breathwork practice called pranayama.

We would practice asana for hours and hours on Fridays and Saturdays.

Exhausted, on Sunday mornings, we would come in and lay down on carefully folded blankets and breathe and meditate.

No matter how sore my muscles had been or how upset my emotions were the week before, by the time Sunday morning rolled around, I felt myself floating in bliss.

I began to teach not just my yoga students but my clients who came to me for natural healing the secrets required to access this blissful state.

The first client who desperately needed the information was an unemployed barber with kidney failure. In his early 30s, he found himself needing three medications to control his high blood pressure.

When the drugs didn't work, the man's kidneys began to fail, and he ended up having to drive himself to a dialysis center at 4:00 a.m. every day for treatment.

The disease, the treatment, the medication and the worry he felt over not being able to provide for his wife and small children had gotten the better of him.

As he sat in my office feeling completely worthless, I prayed for guidance about how best to assist him.

I knew breathwork could lower his blood pressure whereas the medications had failed.

I knew learning how to breathe through his anxiety would give him a tool he could use while strapped to the machine at the dialysis center.

And so I taught him breathwork similar to what I had practiced on those Sunday mornings when I was exhausted from asana practice.

We shortened the length of time so he could experience for himself how much better he could feel in a very brief period.

When you are truly suffering, you don't want to wait one more second to feel better!

To give him a tool he could refer to at home, I wrote down the directions.

I asked a friend to take my iPhone and film me demonstrating the breathing exercises in my garden so I could upload the videos to my website www.unlimitedenergynow.com. That way the barber could receive visual instruct-tion whenever he became unsure if he was doing the breathwork correctly.

Some of my greatest blessings have come to me when I was relentlessly searching for ways to help others. And so it was with my soul friend the unemployed barber. He helped me understand the power of what I had experienced so that I could share these secrets with others.

Chapter 6: Striving to Reach Ground Zero

"Anxiety happens when you think you have to figure out everything all at once. Breathe. You're strong. You got this. Take it day by day."
- Karen Salmansohn

After codifying my personal spin on breathwork for the barber, I began to teach the routine to other clients suffering from anxiety.

One client in particular stands out in my memory: a gay woman who had just learned her partner of more than 20 years had been diagnosed with a terminal illness.

My client and her partner had the same hair color and first name and spent virtually every waking moment together.

The prospect my client faced -- of watching her loved one slip away and ending up alone in life -- triggered terrible anxiety and panic attacks.

"Practice first thing every morning for eight minutes," I advised her about the breathwork.

"Practice again before you go to sleep.

"Put a number on your anxiety before you start. Make it from zero to 10, with zero being no anxiety and 10 being off the chart.

"Even if you don't get to zero right away, knowing you have the power to turn down the volume on your discomfort will give you some hope."

I've used this very same tool in confronting my own bouts of anxiety.

"What would I advise a client to do?" I would ask myself whenever I felt panicky.

Then I would prop myself up in my bed with pillows and practice breathwork.

I would quantify the intensity of my anxiety at the start and notice how my fears dissipated as I continued.

If I couldn't immediately get my discomfort to zero, I would repeat the routine and keep going as long as I could.

And on occasions when I found myself uncomfortable in public places, such as in airport security lines fearing the thick crowds might make me miss my plane, I would practice my breathing exercises.

There are times when your only available tools are your mind and your breath.

Chapter 7:
Your Breath Is Your Power

"The spirit of God has made me and the breath of the Almighty gives me life."
- Job 33:4

In my many years of the study and practice of natural healing, I've experienced a number of highly beneficial therapies, including Brain Gym, Touch for Health, craniosacral therapy, Reiki, hypnosis, plant medicine, flower essences, essential oils, food healing, all kinds of nutritional therapies, homeopathy, body work, multiple systems of physical exercise and multiple systems of kinesiology.

The fact is you may not have the money for a therapist.

You may not trust anyone to hypnotize you. And you may be reluctant to delve into plant medicine or any other therapy that requires you to go outside your comfort zone.

It is so empowering to know you always have your breath and can alter your state of mind naturally without any medication -- legal or illegal -- through breathing exercises.

As a medical intuitive healer, I have worked with every manner of human being you can imagine -- from newborn babies to people in their 90s too sick and feeble to walk, individuals with handicaps, adults with chronic brain injury, teenagers with a variety of anxieties, and others suffering from chronic and even terminal illnesses.

Everybody hurts sometime, and it's my job to help people heal naturally.

That is why I wrote this book for you, dear reader, so you can learn how to empower yourself.

Your breath is your power.

Whether you realize it or not, you derive all your personal power from your breath.

Your confidence, your endurance, the vitality you require to live your life, the very essence of your life itself and your chi, or life energy are stored in your breath.

So why not learn how to use it for your ultimate benefit?

Therefore I give you this, *The Little Book of*

Breathwork.

Even if you don't have asthma, high blood pressure, anxiety, insomnia, sleep apnea or any other physical or mental challenge, you can learn how to achieve the highest states of personal enlightenment, literally relaxing your mind through your breath.

It is my prayer that this book changes your life as radically as breathwork has transformed my existence for the better.

Chapter 8: Prayer for My Readers

"Come to me all you who labor and are heavily burdened and I will give you rest."
- Matthew 11:28

My intention in writing *The Little Book of Breathwork* is to give you tools that you can use anytime, anywhere to feel better naturally for FREE.

I give you the key to your own personal power through your breath.

Along with this book, here is a prayer from my heart to your heart.

Heavenly Father,

I ask that you open the minds of these dear readers so they can discover the power of their breath.

Assist them in learning how to breathe in such a way that they feel calm, grounded, peaceful, powerful and energized.

Teach them patience as they work with their lungs, their heart, their muscles and their subtle energies.

Give them permission to breathe in ways so that they may benefit from the highest possible levels of vitality.

Please empower them to connect their body, mind and spirit through their breath.

Thank you God, thank you God,
thank you God.

Amen.

BOOK II

Think Differently to Breathe Differently

Chapter 1: The 10 Principles of Enlightened Breathwork

"You must master a new way to think before you can master a new way to be."
- Marianne Williamson

As I began to contemplate how to express the full power you possess literally under your nose, I didn't want to write a tome so obtuse, so overwhelming.

I wanted to share my ideas -- such as they are -- in a way that you can fully embrace and incorporate them into your own life.

And that means, keep it simple.

After 24 years of breathing with great awareness, here are the principles I feel underlie all transformational breathwork:

1. Inhale
2. Exhale
3. Breathe in a circle
4. Relax
5. Energize
6. Awaken your awareness

7. Discover yourself
8. Contain your experience
9. Release
10. Feel the bliss

Chapter 2: Enlightened Breathwork Principle One: Inhale

"For my ally is the Force, and a powerful ally it is."
- *Yoda*

As you focus on taking a breath in, you may ask yourself, what exactly am I inhaling? You inhale:

Hope
Joy
Peace
Prosperity
Abundance
Possibility
Knowledge
Wisdom
Tranquility
Oxygen
Energy
Prana
Chi
Life Force
Goodness
Positivity
New ways of thinking

Fresh air
Connection to all that is
Awareness
All that is good
All that transforms you
Higher vibrations
Love
Acceptance
Healing
Vitality
Endurance
Nourishment
Cellular health
Everything my body needs to be healthy
Transformation
Self-acceptance
Radiance
Self-love
Inspiration
Forgiveness
Oneness

As you inhale these positive forces, you can think the following affirmations:

I BREATHE IN ALL THAT COMES TO
ME FOR THE HIGHEST GOOD.
I INHALE THE HIGHEST AND
BEST VIBRATIONS.
I INHALE ALL THE JOY OF

THIS LIFE'S BLESSINGS.
I TAKE IN EVERYTHING I NEED FROM THIS PRECIOUS MOMENT.
I TAKE IN UNCONDITIONAL LOVE.
I FEEL MY DEEP CONNECTION TO THE EARTH, THE STARS AND THE ENTIRE UNIVERSE.
I NOURISH MY CELLS WITH THE VITALITY THEY NEED.
I FILL MY LUNGS WITH SELF-ACCEPTANCE.
I AM INSPIRED TO LIVE MY BEST LIFE.
MY INSPIRATION LEADS ME TO ALL THAT IS HELPFUL FOR MY GROWTH AND DEVELOPMENT.
I AM HUMBLE BEFORE THE BEAUTY AND WONDER OF THE UNIVERSE.
I RADIATE GOODNESS, KINDNESS, HUMILITY AND LOVE EVERYWHERE I GO WITH EVERYONE I AM WITH.
I AM ONE WITH ALL THAT IS.
I AM DEEPLY NOURISHED BY THE ENERGY THAT FLOWS THROUGH THE UNIVERSE.

As you inhale, notice how there is a natural pause at the top of your inhale.

Relax when you get there.

Don’t strain.

Enjoy the way you feel!

Chapter 3: Enlightened Breathwork Principle Two: Exhale

"You will find that it is necessary to let things go; simply for the reason that they are heavy. So let them go, let go of them. I tie no weights to my ankles."

- C. JoyBell C.

As you exhale, you may ask yourself, "What am I exhaling?" You exhale:

Stress
Anxiety
Tension
Pain
Suffering
Depression
Low self-esteem
All that no longer serves you
Trauma
PTSD
Bad memories
Carbon dioxide
Cellular waste
Toxicity
All that holds you back
Restriction

Rules that don't work for you
The past
Bitterness
Resentment
Judgment
Lack of forgiveness
High blood pressure
Pressure
Unrealistic goals
Sorrow
Regret
Self-blame
Blame
Worry

As you exhale, you may want to repeat the following mantras silently to yourself:

I NOW JOYFULLY RELEASE ALL THAT NO LONGER SERVES ME.
I LET GO AND LET GOD.
I ALLOW GOD TO GUIDE ME.
I RELEASE ALL THAT HOLDS ME BACK.
I FORGIVE AS I AM FORGIVEN.
I RELEASE ALL BLAME, BITTERNESS AND JUDGMENT, KNOWING AND EXPERIENCING THE PEACE THAT'S LEFT BEHIND.

I NOW JOYFULLY ACCEPT THIS
PRECIOUS MOMENT.
I LET GO OF THE HABIT OF
OVERTHINKING, JUDGING AND
WORRYING AND SHIFT TO BEING
PRESENT IN THIS MOMENT.
I LIVE IN THE NOW.

As you exhale, notice how there is a natural pause at the bottom of your exhale.

Enjoy this moment!

Allow your mind to slip gently into this quiet space.

Chapter 4: Enlightened Breathwork Principle Three: Breathe in a Circle

"It's the circle of life, and it moves us all,
through despair and hope, through
faith and love, 'til we find our place,
on the path unwinding."
- Elton John

As you bring your awareness to your breath, you'll notice you're actually breathing in a circle.

What do I mean by that? You inhale and there is a natural pause at the top. You exhale and there is a second pause at the bottom.

And then your lungs -- your spirit -- start the whole cycle again even if you don't think too much about it.

When you breathe in a circle, you balance the two sides of your nervous system. As you balance the sympathetic side (by inhaling) and the parasympathetic side (by exhaling), you create the space for your whole being to experience happiness.

In fact, circular breathing is one of the simplest secrets for experiencing happiness.

Your physical body experiences balance, which, in turn, brings your emotions and energy system into greater balance, which, in turn, allows you to experience the joy inherent in this moment.

If you study life energy, you know everything alive moves in a spiraling fashion, circling and circling.

As you follow the natural rise and fall of your breath, what are you breathing in your circle? These things:

Balance
Peace
Calmness
Tranquility
Presence
Oneness
Awareness
Connection
Embodiment
Feeling grounded
Feeling in your body
Feeling your true self
Belonging

As you breathe in a circle, you may want to use the following affirmations:

I AM AT ONE WITH THE UNIVERSE.
I BELONG TO THE FAMILY OF MAN.
I BREATHE IN JOY, I RELEASE STRESS AND TENSION.
I INHALE PEACE, I EXHALE AND LET GO TO MY HIGHEST GOOD.
I INHALE THE PRESENT MOMENT AND ALLOW MYSELF TO EXPERIENCE THE PERFECTION OF ALL THAT IS.
I ALLOW MYSELF TO SIMPLY BE.
I EXPERIENCE MY OWN BEINGNESS IN THIS MOMENT BREATHING.
I TRUST THE DIVINE UNFOLDING OF THE UNIVERSE AS IT FLOWS THROUGH ME NOW IN THIS PRECIOUS LIFE OF MINE.
I TRUST THE CIRCLE OF LIFE.

As you breathe in a circle, let go of any need to rush, push or strain.

Enjoy the way you feel.

Relax and feel the way your soul receives comfort from your very own breath!

Chapter 5: Enlightened Breathwork Principle Four: Relax

"God comes near and breathes the breath of heaven into our weary souls."

\- *Nan Jones*

As you practice breathwork, you may notice you naturally feel more and more relaxed.

You don't need to take a drug (legal or illegal), call friends (even though they may be helpful), consider a therapist's advice, trek to a foreign land to consult a guru, undergo hypnosis, have a surgical lobotomy, distract yourself with overwork, exercise to the point of exhaustion or take up any other form of self-numbing activity, no matter how appealing or even addictive those previous approaches may have been.

When you relax, you activate your parasympathetic nervous system.

Because you are hardwired to survive, not to relax, you have to make an effort to relax.

The simplest way to access your parasympathetic nervous system is to breathe into your belly.

And how do you breathe into your belly? You can start with these simple techniques:

Technique One. Lie on your stomach. Turn your head to one side to relax your neck. As you inhale, feel your belly pushing naturally against the floor. As you exhale, feel your muscles relax.

Technique Two. Lie on your back. Put your hands on your belly. As you inhale, feel your belly expand. Relax as you exhale, feeling your belly drop in.

Technique Three. Lie on your back. Put a book or other object on your belly. As you inhale, notice how the book or object naturally rises a little bit. As you exhale, notice how the book or object naturally drops down.

Depending on how stressed you feel, it could take anywhere from a few seconds to a few minutes to access your belly breath. As you breathe into your belly and relax, you may want to say these affirmations silently to yourself:

IT FEELS GOOD TO RELAX.
I GIVE MYSELF PERMISSION TO RELAX AS MUCH AS POSSIBLE.
THE MORE I RELAX, THE MORE WISDOM AND BLESSINGS FLOW THROUGH TO ME.
AS I RELAX, I RELEASE MY RESISTANCE TO WHAT IS.
I RELEASE MY RESISTANCE, ALLOW MYSELF TO BE FULLY PRESENT AND FEEL ALL THE BLESSINGS OF BEING MYSELF IN THIS LIFETIME.
I LOVE THE ENERGY THAT FLOWS THROUGH ME.

When we tense our diaphragm, it is difficult for us to use our full lung capacity. The consequences can include fatigue, asthma, sleep apnea, insomnia or simple anxiety and depression.

The more you learn to relax, the more you turn down the overall tension your muscles are required to carry.

When you relax, you have more energy to live your life.

Breathe into your belly, fully relax, let go of

judgment and allow yourself to feel how good you can feel in this moment.

Ah!

It is good to be you breathing into your body in this precious lifetime.

Chapter 6: Enlightened Breathwork Principle Five: Energize

"Your heart knows the way. Run in that direction."

- Rumi

The more energy you learn to circulate through your very own body, the better mother, father, brother, sister, son, daughter, worker, boss, friend, aunt, uncle and person you can be. The more energy you have, the more you can enjoy being you!

Whatever you do -- whether you're a yoga teacher or a bricklayer -- requires tons of energy, and some of us require more energy, especially if your pursuits involve working with others – e.g., as healers, teachers, homeroom monitors, nannies, leaders, CEOs, coaches, or ministers.

In fact, the more people you work with, the more essential it is for you to keep your own energy level as strong as it can be.

That's because it's a law of physics that energy always flows from the highest to the lowest potential.

If your own energy is low and you try to do healing work with others, forget about it.

If your energy sucks and you try to teach a class, well, good luck with that.

If you have allowed your energy to become depleted through lack of self-care and you're a mother, well, you already know how that's going to turn out -- not very well.

One of the simplest free forms of energy is right under your nose -- literally.

When I do a medical intuitive reading, one of the things I frequently look at is what is known as your energy body. It includes your breath as well as your acupuncture system and the energy vortexes known as chakras.

Your breath is the common denominator through which your life force flows.

As you practice breathwork, you increase the flow of oxygen to every cell in your body.

And that simple act gives you more energy, but there's even a little more to it than that.

We know that when you breathe into your belly, your parasympathetic nervous system is activated, and you relax.

Yes, you want to relax, but sometimes you also need to take action, which requires alertness, stamina, endurance and focus.

The way to activate your sympathetic nervous system is to breathe fully into your upper chest.

When you get into a shower, you quickly figure out whether to turn the hot knob one way and the cold knob another way. In the same fashion, you can learn to use your breath to regulate your activity as well as how you feel.

When you need more energy, breathe more fully into your upper chest, expanding your lungs as much as possible.

As you're getting energized with upper-chest breathing, you may want to say the following affirmations:

I RECEIVE ALL THE ENERGY I NEED TO EXCEL IN THIS SITUATION.

I FOCUS MY MIND AND ENERGY TO COMPLETE THE TASKS AT HAND WITH EASE AND GRACE.

I AM A CLEAR AND PERFECT CHANNEL FOR THE PRECISE AMOUNT OF ENERGY I NEED IN THIS MOMENT.

I ENERGIZE MY MIND AND BODY AND ENJOY THE WAY I FEEL.

THE FORCE IS WITH ME.

I RADIATE ENERGY AND UPLIFT EVERYONE AROUND ME.

Chapter 7: Enlightened Breathwork Principle Six: Awaken Your Awareness

"Realize deeply that the present moment is all you ever have. Make the Now the primary focus on your life."

- *Eckhart Tolle*

As you breathe fully and completely, inhaling and exhaling, noticing the circle of prana in your body, you may observe how you feel more in the present moment than ever before.

When your mind focuses on the past, you remain stuck in guilt, grief, depression and regret.

When your mind races ahead into the future, your worries and mental pictures of all the possible disastrous outcomes may flood your mind with anxiety.

And as you breathe, simply sitting or lying with yourself and breathing, you may start to notice the quality of your existence in the here and now.

You feel the urge to scratch your cheek.

You notice the light in the room.

You slow down your thoughts, possibly even clearing them for a few precious moments, and space appears in your mind.

In that moment, awareness can drop in.

Some people may call the experience "intuition." Others may refer to it as your soul guidance.

As you have managed to quiet your ego mind and set aside the habit of mentally grasping everything around you, you notice yourself being you in the present.

You may hear the birds singing in the trees.

You may feel the breeze through your hair.

All of a sudden, life has come to a momentary standstill, and the quality of your existence becomes immensely enjoyable.

You didn't read a single spiritual text. You simply stayed present with yourself and suddenly began feeling as wise as a Jedi.

As you awaken your awareness through

breathing, you may want to repeat the following affirmations silently to yourself:

I BRING MY ENERGY INTO THE
PRESENT MOMENT NOW.
I AM ONE WITH ALL THAT IS.
I EXPERIENCE THE JOY AVAILABLE TO
ME IN THIS PRESENT MOMENT.
I ALLOW MYSELF TO MERGE WITH
THE ENERGY OF ALL THAT IS.
I FEEL MY ONENESS.
I CONNECT WITH THE ENERGY OF ALL
THE EARTH AND THE STARS IN THE
SKY AND THE UNIVERSE.
I ALLOW THE ENERGY OF THE
UNIVERSE TO FLOW THROUGH ME.
I CHANNEL THE ENERGY AND THE
WISDOM OF THE UNIVERSE FOR THE
HIGHEST GOOD OF ALL.
I AM ONE WITH THE LIFE FORCE OF
THE UNIVERSE.

As you notice yourself becoming more and more aware, enjoy the way you feel!

Chapter 8: Enlightened Breathwork Principle Seven: Discover Yourself

"Until you make the unconscious conscious, it will direct your life and you will call it fate."

\- *Carl Jung*

As you are inhaling, exhaling, noticing the circle of flowing energy, relaxing, allowing yourself to restore your energy and awakening your awareness to the present moment, a funny thing can happen: You may start feeling the way you really feel!

Sometimes of course, the way you feel may be absolutely fabulous.

Warm.
Snuggly.
Open.
Peaceful.

And yet the truth is that life isn't always easy.

You may notice tension in your chest.

Constriction around your head.

A tightness in your jaw.

Your feet may feel as heavy as lead.

Your eyes may feel so blurry you can barely open them.

And all the emergency emotions you have been running from, overworking to avoid, and anesthetizing yourself to suppress may suddenly come welling up.

And that's OK. This is when you should tell yourself certain very helpful facts.

It takes a lot of energy to suppress, repress, tamp down or try to keep a lid on what's really going on. As you breathe, you create a safe space to discover yourself.

While you notice what's coming up -- your grief, anger, anxiety, regret or even floods of emotions so intense you can't quite put them all into words -- please allow yourself to be you in this moment.

As you discover yourself, you may want to use the following affirmations:

IT IS SAFE TO BE ME IN THIS LIFETIME.
I EMBRACE MY HUMANITY.
I LOVE MYSELF JUST AS I AM IN THIS PRECIOUS MOMENT.
I GIVE MYSELF PERMISSION TO FEEL THE WAY I REALLY FEEL.
I ALLOW MY TRUE SELF TO SHOW UP.
I SHOW UP FOR MY TRUE SELF AS I PRACTICE BEING REAL WITH MYSELF.
I AM CONSCIOUS OF MYSELF AS A LIVING, BREATHING BEING.

As you discover yourself, you will notice that the intensity of your negative emotions frequently decreases as you continue to breathe and allow yourself to be who you really are and feeling what you actually feel.

Hold yourself with tenderness in this moment.

Tender is the moment when you discover how you're really feeling.

Chapter 9: Enlightened Breathwork Principle Eight: Contain Your Experience

"I'm safe inside this container called me."
- Haruki Murakami

Now that you're busy inhaling, exhaling, noticing the circle of energy flowing in and through you, relaxing, energizing your cells, awakening your awareness and discovering your true self, you may begin to feel a bit overwhelmed at times.

The energy of all you have been avoiding comes rushing into your awareness. How can you handle it?

The secret is to contain your experience. One way to do that is to set your intention. Here are a few steps you can follow:

Technique One. Before beginning your breathwork, decide how long you will practice. You could limit the experience to just five minutes or go for half an hour. Then, even if negative emotions arise that feel too painful, you know it will all be over at the prescribed time. You can walk away from the experience by shifting your attention to another activity.

Technique Two. Visualize an actual container. It could be as small as a china teacup or as huge as a big green garbage dumpster. Then allow yourself to feel only as much emotion as it takes to fill up your container. When your container feels full, visualize yourself emptying it. You could see yourself burying the teacup or the city sanitation department driving up and hauling off the dumpster. Whether you visualize a small or a large container, you put a limit on how much you will allow yourself to feel.

Both techniques keep you in control.

When you feel in control over what you feel, you won't be overwhelmed by the intensity.

You also won't need to try to escape the reality of it.

You get to experience what it feels like to be strong enough to be you.

As you contain your experience, you may want to use the following affirmations:

I AM IN CHARGE OF THE
WAY I FEEL.
I AM SAFE FEELING WHAT I FEEL.
IT IS SAFE FOR ME TO EXPERIENCE MY
DEEP-DOWN FEELINGS, KNOWING
AND EXPERIENCING THAT MY SOUL
KNOWS WHAT
I CAN HANDLE.
MY SOUL GUIDES MY FEELING
EXPERIENCE.
I ALLOW MY SOUL TO OPEN ME UP TO
ALL OF LIFE NOW THAT I FEEL SAFER
AND SAFER.
IT IS SAFE FOR ME TO BE FULLY ALIVE
NOW IN THIS BODY
IN THIS LIFETIME.

Chapter 10: Enlightened Breathwork Principle Nine: Release

"The calmest person in the room is always the most powerful."

- *Eben Pagan*

As you're inhaling, exhaling, relaxing, feeling more energized, discovering your true self and creating the container of your safe experience, you begin to release way down deep.

Often our life's traumas have become so deeply buried that our conscious minds can't access them. Sometimes we may even sense that something big and bad is in there -- a feeling, a hunch, a dread -- but not feel ready to let it go.

You have to realize that your psyche is much stronger than you may think. You may think you can only handle *this* much, but your soul actually knows best.

And you may be deeply invested in the story you've been telling yourself all these years. You've told the story so many times you've got it memorized by now.

Either way -- whether you have repressed what happened or can recite it by heart -- you can release the trauma's energy without uttering a single word by using breathwork. That is because your energy system holds the vibration of everything that has occurred in your lifetime.

If you feel your nervous system is chronically amped up, manifesting as stress, chronic tension, high blood pressure, insomnia, depression, anxiety or simply feeling awful all the time, you can gradually turn down the intensity by releasing the energy with breathwork.

How do I know that for certain? Because I myself am not the same person I was when I started practicing breathwork years ago.

And I have watched my students -- even ones diagnosed with high blood pressure and asthma not alleviated by medications prescribed by their medical doctors -- literally breathe their problems away.

I remember one lady who had suffered high blood pressure for 10 years. She had done everything she could think of -- take drugs, go on a diet, exercise daily -- but only when she came to my yoga class and learned how to breathe properly did her high blood pressure suddenly and mysteriously evaporate.

When my student went back to her medical doctor for a checkup, the nurses kept checking her blood pressure. They would make her sit down, stand up, and let them take the measurements again and again.

Gone!

The high blood pressure numbers they had been waiting to measure had been replaced by totally normal blood pressure.

Learning to breathe properly had done for her what taking a number of drugs, losing weight and trying various kinds of exercise could not accomplish.

As you breathe, you release what ails you.

You don't have to figure it out.

You don't have to remember the story.

All you really have to do is give yourself

permission to breathe into the possibility that your soul knows when and how to release the trauma for your highest good.

As you practice releasing with your breathwork, you may use the following affirmations:

I JOYFULLY RELEASE ALL
THE ENERGY THAT HAS
HELD ME BACK.
I GIVE MYSELF PERMISSION TO
RELEASE WHAT IS NO
LONGER IN MY HIGHEST GOOD.
I LET GO AND ALLOW THE WISDOM OF
MY SOUL
TO GUIDE ME NOW.
I RELEASE THE PAST
AND FORGIVE EVERYONE
WHO HAS EVER HURT ME.
I FORGIVE MYSELF.
I FORGIVE ALL OTHERS.
I AM FREE!

Chapter 11: Enlightened Breathwork Principle Ten: Feel the Bliss

"Breathe in deeply to bring your mind home to your body."

-Thich Nhat Hanh

As you are inhaling, exhaling, enjoying the wonderful flow of energy circulating in your body, relaxing, feeling so much more energetic, discovering yourself in a safe, contained experience and releasing what no longer serves you, you may notice yourself feeling more and more blissful.

Bliss.

Pure bliss.

A bliss that feels so good you couldn't even begin to describe it in words.

As you breathe, you let go of ego interference and enter the realm of experiencing your own beautiful soul.

The yogis have a name for this. They call the soul your Anandamaya kosha, or the body of bliss.

I told you at the beginning we wouldn't be using fancy or obtuse terms, but I'm definitely going to give you some background so you can understand where all this information comes from.

I'm referencing the yogis to let you know that other people in other traditions have noticed that when we relax into pure spiritual awareness, we begin to feel flat-out amazing!

That is what I felt on those Sunday mornings when I practiced breathwork and meditation.

That is what I feel when I'm by myself in the dark of the night practicing my breathwork in silence.

Bliss is the way you can feel if you simply follow the 10 principles I've laid out for you, breathing along as best you can.

Even if you start out FINE – Frustrated, Insecure, Neurotic and Emotional -- if you keep at it, breathing through your experience for better or worse, sooner or later the negative feelings will indeed fall away, and you will enter the peace that surpasses all understanding.

I think the sages call this "the peace that surpasses all understanding" because you cannot access this state of bliss by figuring anything out. Your ego cannot take you there.

Your ego is like a showboat -- shiny, showy, thinking itself so important. Even if you had a full-throttle high IQ, your ego can only take you so far.

But your breath, that's different. Your breath can take you into a place where you feel so happy, so at one with all that is, that all is naturally forgiven. Pain and suffering simply fall away, and you experience an inner knowledge that everything that has ever happened to you has all been in divine order.

As you feel the bliss, you may want to use the following affirmations:

THANK YOU, GOD, FOR ALLOWING ME TO EXPERIENCE THE TRANSCENDENT BLISS OF BEING FULLY ALIVE IN THIS BODY IN THIS LIFETIME.
I GIVE MYSELF PERMISSION TO FEEL GOOD.

AS I FEEL THE BLISS OF MY PEACEFUL EXISTENCE, I
RADIATE LOVE AND LIGHT TO EVERYONE AROUND ME.
I AM A CLEAR AND
PERFECT CHANNEL FOR THE LOVE AND LIGHT OF GOD.
I AM HEALED. I AM WHOLE.
I AM ONE WITH THE UNIVERSE.
I AM GRATEFUL FOR THIS OPPORTUNITY TO BE FULLY ALIVE AT THIS TIME IN THIS BODY, KNOWING AND EXPERIENCING MY BLESSED PLACE IN THE UNIVERSE AND CONTRIBUTING TO THE WELL-BEING OF EACH AND EVERYONE AROUND ME.
I LOVE MY LIFE. I AM SO BLESSED.
THANK YOU GOD, THANK
YOU GOD, THANK YOU GOD.

As you feel the bliss into which you have breathed yourself, set your intention to use this high vibrational energy for the greatest good of all.

Chi, prana, energy -- whatever you want to call it -- has its own intelligence and will take you wherever your soul calls you.

Chapter 12: What Is the Pranamaya Kosha?

"Absorbing more oxygen means greater vitality."
-Moshe Feldenkrais

As you explore the 10 principles of enlightened breathwork, a funny thing will start happening: You will become aware of yourself as a being of energy.

Up to this point, you may have thought of yourself as a soul with a body of flesh and blood. As you explore your own breath, however, you will start experiencing your own energy body, your own specific frequency.

Let me put this into perspective for you.

Studying yoga and practicing breathwork have had a profound effect on my work as a medical intuitive healer, in addition to the obvious benefit of keeping myself physically healthy, calm and grounded. The way that yogis look at a body has totally transformed the way I consider a human being.

There are five levels of your body. In yoga, we refer to the levels as your koshas, or sheaths.

A good way to visualize how this works is to remember the traditional Russian dolls. The decorated wooden dolls feature a larger doll on the outside encasing any number of smaller figures on the inside.

You lift the top off to remove one doll casing only to reveal another version looking similar but different (and obviously smaller) before arriving at the final, tiniest whole doll without any divisions.

And so it is with your koshas.

Your five koshas include:

Annamaya kosha. Your **physical body** includes your organs, bones, blood and everything you consider solid. It's what most people have in mind when they think of their body, but the way I look at you goes far beyond your material body.

Pranamaya kosha. Your **energy body** includes the bioenergetic field surrounding your physical body. It contains your chakras, the acupuncture system and your breath. Your pranamaya kosha infuses your physical body with life force.

As you practice the 10 principles of enlightened breathwork, you will be balancing your pranamaya kosha.

Your energy body is your personal frequency. It is as unique to you as your fingerprint.

Intuitively, you have experienced this yourself because even among the people you love, you've noticed one person's energy is different from another.

Manomaya kosha. Your **emotional body** is actually the largest part of you. You store emotions in your organs, muscles and other parts of your physical body.

Your emotional body is so powerful it can shut down or affect the functioning of any physical process. That's why resolving the emotions that have been bothering you is essential to your long-term well-being.

As you'll discover by practicing breathwork, you can release buried emotions, trauma, and even post-traumatic stress disorder (PTSD) through deep breathing. You don't need to talk about what happened (although talking may be helpful). You don't even need to remember what happened (although your curious ego mind may want to know).

Simply by breathing into your body's stuck energy, you have the power to release a tremendous amount of repressed emotional material.

And you don't need a therapist to do it, as helpful as all kinds of counselors may be. All you need is your willingness to breathe and let go.

Vijnamaya kosha. Your **mental body** is the seat of your ego, wisdom and judgment. This is where you hold your thoughts, opinions and beliefs. Your mind tells you a story about your life. The story either heals you or kills you.

With recognition and understanding, you can direct your mind to think in ways that bring balance, inner peace and calmness to the rest of your being.

As you practice the 10 principles of enlightened breathing, you may notice how your thoughts and beliefs affect your breath.

For example, if you think a stressful thought, you may notice yourself holding your breath.

By changing your breathing patterns, you have the opportunity to create the space where you see your personal story from a higher perspective and let go of the thought patterns that have kept you stuck.

Anandamaya kosha. Your **spiritual body** is the part of you beyond all space and time. Your soul existed before you were incarnated into your physical body in this lifetime and will continue to exist once what you think of as your body has passed away.

Eternal, transcendent and naturally blissful, your spirit directs your entire life experience. As you discover your soul purpose, the rest of your life begins to make more sense. Challenges become easier to endure. You develop tenacity and equanimity and feel at one with all that is.

As you practice noticing your bliss as you breathe, you have the opportunity to experience the grace of your anandamaya kosha.

Chapter 13:
How Everything Works Together

"Stop acting so small. You are the universe in ecstatic motion."

- Rumi

Now let's go back to your pranamaya kosha.

Once you understand your energy body controls the amount of life force that flows through your physical body, you will want to do everything in your power to maintain a healthy level of chi.

Your chi level is so important that it's the first thing I look at when I do a medical intuitive reading. When you enjoy a high level of chi, that's the equivalent of having a good savings account at the bank.

You may be exposed to viruses, bad bacteria or any manner of accidents or other illnesses, but your physical body can recover quickly and easily when you maintain good personal chi.

You also can think of your pranamaya kosha as the energetic blueprint that creates your physical reality.

An imbalance in your energy body will eventually filter down to a disturbance in your physical body. That's because all illnesses and diseases begin in our energy field and filter from the spiritual into the mental, into the emotional, into the energy body and finally into your physical body.

When you heal, you push the disturbance out of your physical body, through your energy body, back past your emotional and mental processes and out through your soul level.

If you get stuck by neglecting or overlooking any of your five "bodies," you delay the healing process and/or may never fully recover.

Breathing exercises are some of the simplest ways to regulate the level of prana through your energy body. I recommend breathwork because your breath is available to you anytime, anywhere -- no drugs, no natural healing remedy, no practitioner required.

You can breathe through the emotional energies that you've stuck anywhere in your being even if you aren't consciously aware of the traumas you're releasing.

Your breath is the cheapest, easiest, most accessible power tool you have at your disposal to increase your life force.

As you learn to regulate your breath, you can calm your mind when you feel too hyper or turn up your physical energy level when you feel exhausted.

Chapter 14:
Breathe to Balance Your Energy

"Deep breaths are like little love notes to your body."
- Kelly Rae Roberts

As you breathe, you not only engage your respiratory system but also balance the flow of energy through your chakras, the centers of spiritual power in the human body.

You have seven major chakras that correspond to the seven major endocrine glands.

Balancing your chakras by regulating the flow of breath can have profound beneficial effects on your entire mental, physical and emotional well-being.

Your breath flows to your chakras through invisible energy channels known as nadis. Experts disagree on the precise number of nadis in your body -- anywhere from 72,000 to 350,000 -- but all agree the subtle energy flows originate in your navel.

Here are three of the most important nadis:

Ida. Your ida ends in your left nostril and left lung. It corresponds with the lunar, yin energies in your body and the right side of your brain. When you breathe primarily out of your left nostril, you activate your parasympathetic nervous system. You become more passive and internally focused. Your body temperature, blood pressure, cortisol and testosterone levels decrease.

Pingala. Your pingala ends in your right nostril and right lung. It corresponds with the solar, yang energies in your body and with the left side of your brain. When you breathe primarily out of your right nostril, you activate your sympathetic nervous system. You become more active and focused on the external world. Your body temperature, cortisol, testosterone, blood pressure and heart rate increase.

Sushumna. Your sushumna corresponds with your spinal cord. It serves as the central axis of your energy body and is your most important nadi. Energy runs through your sushumna from the base of your spine to the crown of your head.

When you are healthy, you alternate your nostril dominance every two to two-and-a-half hours. Part of what keeps you healthy is your chronobiology, maintaining healthy rhythms in your body.

When you become unhealthy, however, you may breathe primarily out of one nostril or the other, which may indicate an imbalance in your nervous system.

When you become stuck in your parasympathetic nervous system, you may feel exhausted and depressed.

When you become stuck in your sympathetic nervous system, you may feel wired and anxious.

As we practice breathing deeply through both nostrils, we balance the two sides of our nervous system and produce an inner state of equanimity in our energy body. There will be a corresponding increased flow of prana throughout your physical body as well as a feeling of calmness, clear-headedness and inner peace.

Disturbances in your breathing patterns may lead to anxiety, depression, insomnia, sleep apnea, high blood pressure and many other conditions.

BOOK III

Eight Minutes to Inner Peace

Chapter 1: My Favorite Breathwork Routine

"Quiet the mind and the soul will speak."
- Ma Jaya Sati Bhagavati

As I have taught and practiced breathwork and yoga over the past 24 years, I came to put together a simple, easy routine that empowers anyone to shift their energy in a rapid period of time. It's the same breathing routine I taught the unemployed barber with kidney failure and the gay woman who was suffering from anxiety as she witnessed her life partner slipping away into a degenerative and fatal disease.

I came to call it "Eight Minutes to Inner Peace."

I know that when we feel bad, we all want quick tools to shift out of our discomfort. While it now seems the average human being's attention span can be shorter than that of a goldfish, our natural healing remedies need to keep pace.

Here is the simplest way I know to make a profound change in the way you feel.

Start by sitting or lying down in a comfortable position.

1. ONE MINUTE: Focus on lengthening your inhale.
2. ONE MINUTE: Focus on lengthening your exhale.
3. ONE MINUTE: Focus on making your inhale and exhale equally long and deep. (Now sit up for the remaining steps.)
4. ONE MINUTE: Bellows Breath. Inhale into your belly, and exhale forcibly by contracting your solar plexus.
5. ONE MINUTE: Breath of Fire. While inhaling and exhaling rapidly, pump your diaphragm. Your inhale will happen naturally.
6. ONE MINUTE: Alternate nostril breathing. Inhale through your right nostril. With the thumb of your right hand, close the right nostril. Exhale through your left nostril. With the ring finger of your right hand, close the left nostril. Exhale through your right nostril. Use your thumb to close your right nostril. Exhale through the left nostril. Use your ring

finger to close the left. Repeat.

7. ONE MINUTE: Bumblebee Breath. Place your pointer and middle fingers on your forehead. Place your thumbs on your ear flaps, and close your ears. Place your ring finger lightly on your closed eyelids. Let you little finger rest on your cheekbones. Make a humming sound like a bee.
8. ONE MINUTE: Ocean Breath. Open your mouth, relax your jaw. Inhale and make the sound of the ocean in the back of your throat. Exhale and make the ocean sound. Close your lips and continue making the sound.

If you would like to watch videos explaining how to do each breath, please visit this link: http://unlimitedenergynow.com/eightminutes-to-inner-peace-breathing-exercisespranayama/

If you're unsure what I just described, don't worry. I'm getting ready to explain it to you in more detail.

Although I recommend performing each breathwork sequence in this session for at least one minute, as time permits you can enjoy each breathing technique longer.

Notice the exercises that feel best for you. They may vary from day to day and from season to season.

Chapter 2:
Heal Your Mind and Body with Your Breath

"The soul always knows what to do to heal itself. The challenge is to silence the mind."
- Caroline Myss

Although all breathwork is beneficial, yogis have developed a deep understanding about which breathing exercises activate the opposite sides of your nervous system as well as the different energy centers in your body.

You can tailor the breathwork routine to meet your specific health challenges.

High Blood Pressure

To lower high blood pressure, I recommend you practice all eight breathing exercises in Eight Minutes to Inner Peace twice a day, preferably first thing in the morning and again before going to bed.

Also, turn to one or all of the exercises during the day anytime you feel angry or anxious -- two emotions known to drive up blood pressure.

If you don't want to do the whole routine or have only a few minutes, I recommend you focus on:

- Breathing into your belly to activate your parasympathetic nervous system
- Exhaling
- Circular breathing
- Ocean Breath

From my observations, I will tell you that most people with high blood pressure don't exhale properly.

If you suffer from high blood pressure, you tend to stay stuck in your sympathetic nervous system. You need to balance the system, which is why circular breathing and Ocean Breath will be so helpful to you.

Low Blood Pressure

If you suffer from low blood pressure, practice the Eight Minutes to Inner Peace exercises twice a day, preferably first thing in the morning and before bed.

Also, turn to one or all of the exercises anytime you feel disempowered or have fallen into low self-esteem -- the primary emotions that cause low blood pressure. I recommend you focus on:

- Breathing into your upper chest to activate your sympathetic nervous system
- Inhaling
- Bellows Breath
- Breath of Fire

If you suffer from low blood pressure, you may also suffer from depression. You tend to be stuck in the parasympathetic nervous system, which is why Bellows Breath and Breath of Fire will be so helpful to you.

Anxiety

If you suffer from anxiety, practice the exercises twice a day, preferably first thing in the morning and before going to bed. Also, turn to one or all of the exercises anytime you feel anxious.

See if you can identify where your muscles are tightening up. You may be able to notice where you're holding the energy or anxiety. Or you may simply feel tight and constricted everywhere.

As you bring the light of awareness to where you're holding the tension, breathe into those places and let it go. I recommend you focus on:

- Breathing into your belly to activate your parasympathetic nervous system
- Circular breathing
- Alternate nostril breathing
- Bumblebee Breath

You tend to be stuck in your sympathetic nervous system. Even if you know you should relax or would like to relax, you may not be able to do so.

Circular breathing will help to balance the two sides of your nervous system so that you can relax.

Alternate nostril breathing will balance the right and left hemispheres of your brain so you can get out of the habit of repetitive thinking and find whole brain solutions.

Bumblebee Breath will quiet your overactive ego mind so that you can let go into silence.

Depression

Practice the Eight Minute exercises twice a day, preferably first thing in the morning and before going to bed. Also, turn to one or all of the exercises anytime you feel depressed.

See if you can identify where you're holding stuck energy in your body. Breathe into those places, and let the feelings go during the exercises.

I recommend you focus on:

- Breathing into your upper chest to activate your sympathetic nervous system
- Alternate nostril breathing
- Bumblebee Breath
- Ocean Breath

When you feel depressed, you're stuck in the parasympathetic nervous system. Breathing into your upper chest will help to activate stagnant chi.

Alternate nostril breathing will balance the right and left hemispheres of your brain so that you can find whole brain solutions.

Bumblebee Breath will calm your ego mind and allow you to experience inner peace.

Ocean Breath will balance your nervous system and give you the energy to move forward.

Fatigue

Practice the exercises twice a day, preferably first thing in the morning and before bed. Also, turn to one or all of the exercises anytime you feel your energy drop.

See if you can feel any places in your body where your energy is stagnant or stuck. Allow your breath to open all your energy channels as you practice.

I recommend you focus on:

- Breathing from your navel into your arms and legs and up into your head
- Circular breathing
- Bumblebee Breath
- Ocean Breath

In yoga, there is a flow of breath, called a vayu, that originates in your navel. It's your vyana vayu that distributes chi all over your body.

When you breathe from the center of your belly up into your head, down through your legs and out into your arms, you energize your whole being.

Circular breathing can balance your nervous system and help you to feel happy.

Bumblebee Breath will calm the overactive ego mind that has exhausted you.

Ocean Breath will give you the energy to move forward.

Asthma

Because you may have difficulty breathing, be sure to avoid straining. Do not push. Do not judge yourself. Just do the best you can.

Practice the Eight Minutes exercises twice a day, preferably first thing in the morning and before bed. Also, turn to one or all of the exercises anytime you experience shortness of breath.

I recommend you focus on:

- Belly breathing
- Inhaling
- Exhaling
- Circular breathing

It's crucial you learn how to breathe into your belly because your breath may have been stuck in your upper chest possibly your entire life. In one of my classes, an 81-year-old yoga student with asthma transformed his breathing by learning the simple technique of belly breathing.

You also may be affected by environmental allergies. If so, ask a natural health practitioner to look for mold in your home or workplace, which could be adversely affecting your lungs and making it harder for you to breathe.

Explore whether any food sensitivities such as cow's milk are affecting your lungs. Realize you may need to address other aspects to rid yourself of asthma.

Above all, be patient with yourself.

Sleep Apnea
Practice the Eight Minutes exercises before you go to bed. After completing all eight exercises, lie in bed and continue to practice circular breathing until you fall asleep.

I recommend you focus on:

- Inhaling
- Exhaling
- Circular breathing

Breathing Difficulties

Even without a medical doctor's diagnosis, you may have noticed you have difficulty breathing. If so, I recommend you blow your nose thoroughly before practicing breathwork. Give yourself permission to blow your nose again between each exercise, as pranayama will open up your airways.

If your nose is very congested, you may want to do a nasal rinse before starting the Eight Minutes exercises. You can mix salt into warm water and irrigate your nasal passages.

I recommend you focus on:

- Inhaling
- Exhaling
- Circular breathing

If the exercises feel difficult, stop and blow your nose. It's OK to be a beginner! As you practice a little bit every day, you'll notice it gets easier to breathe. You'll experience higher levels of energy while also feeling calm and peaceful.

Chapter 3: Eight Minutes to Inner Peace Exercise One: Inhale Deeply for More Energy

"Slow breathing is like an anchor in the midst of an emotional storm: the anchor won't make the storm go away, but it will hold you steady until it passes."

- *Russ Harris*

Here's how to practice inhaling:

1. Either sit up straight with your chest spread wide, or lie comfortably.
2. If you are sitting down, make sure you press your shoulders back and lift the tip of your sternum so that your lungs can expand completely.
3. If you are lying down, make sure you're on your back with your chest spread wide and your lungs open.
4. Place your hands on your belly.
5. As you inhale, feel your belly and rib cage expand and your chest widen.
6. If it's helpful, keep one hand on your belly, and allow the other hand to alternate between your rib cage and

upper chest.
7. Allow the exhale to do whatever it's going to do.
8. Do not strain.
9. Feel yourself breathing three-dimensionally – *i.e.,* into your belly, ribs and upper chest.
10. Enjoy the way you feel!

Learning how to inhale completely can dramatically increase your energy.

As you learn how to use your full lung capacity, you'll increase the oxygen available to your brain, heart, lungs and every cell of your body.

I remember years ago, I had a friend who was a naturopath. One day he borrowed a device from his local hospital that measured oxygen intake. He said most of the people sitting at desks in his office had such low cellular oxygen that they would have required extra oxygen had they been hospitalized.

Many people aren't aware how our habit of slumping collapses our lungs, decreases the oxygen to our brain and body and dramatically restricts the supply of available energy.

Naturally, the first thing you have to do when you want to increase your energy is to learn how to inhale. As we mentioned earlier, your inhale has a direct effect on both sides of your nervous system:

Sympathetic nervous system. This part of the system responds to stress. Every neuron in your sympathetic nervous system is connected to at least 20 other neurons.

Parasympathetic nervous system. This part of the system allows you to relax. Every neuron in your parasympathetic nervous system is connected to only about five other neurons.

When we're healthy, the two sides of your nervous system are balanced.

What's a simple way to tell if your nervous system is balanced at this moment? All you have to do is check your breath.

If it's easy to inhale but difficult to exhale, you're stuck in your sympathetic nervous system. That is usually the case for people with high blood pressure, anxiety or stress.

If you notice your inhale is shallow but you're

exhaling longer than you inhale, you are stuck in your parasympathetic nervous system. That could be the case if you're feeling depressed.

Most people breathe primarily into their upper chest and don't use their full lung capacity.

As you practice filling your entire lungs with oxygen, you will feel more energized, inspired and ready for anything.

Chapter 4:
Eight Minutes to Inner Peace
Exercise Two: Exhale and Let It All Go

"Inhale the present, exhale the past and the future."

- *Leticia Rae*

Here's how to practice exhaling:

1. Either sit up straight with your chest spread wide, or lie comfortably.
2. If you're sitting down, make sure you press your shoulders back and lift the tip of your sternum so that your lungs can expand completely.
3. If you're lying down, make sure you are on your back with your chest spread and your lungs open.
4. Place your hands on your belly.
5. Inhale and allow your inhale to do whatever it's going to do.
6. As you lengthen your exhale, let the air out of your lungs, and feel your belly come back toward your spine, relaxing more deeply.
7. Do not strain.

8. Enjoy the way you feel!

If you listen carefully to a person who is highly stressed, they frequently don't exhale properly.

When we exhale, we have the opportunity to let go of stress and tension at a very deep level.

Failing to exhale properly is a common symptom of high blood pressure.

When you don't exhale all the way, you don't fully release carbon dioxide out of your pulmonary capillaries. Too much carbon dioxide, in turn, adversely affects your entire body chemistry and can damage your organs.

Take a deep breath while you are reading this chapter.

Then let it go.

Ahhh!

How do you feel now? A little better, I hope!

Your nervous system is programmed to survive, not to relax. Therefore, when we want to relax, we must make a conscious effort to do so.

The first place to begin with deep relaxation is to learn how to let it all go with your exhale.

Years ago I had a computer monitor from the Institute of HeartMath that measured cardiac coherence, the degree of harmony in your mind-body system. Today the same outfit produces biofeedback devices that connect to your smartphone.

According to research reported in the magazine *Scientific American*, deep breathing increases the activity of your vagus nerve, a part of the parasympathetic nervous system that controls your blood pressure.

If you look at an electrocardiogram (or EKG) for anyone with high blood pressure, you can easily see they don't exhale properly. It may have become such a long-term habit that they don't even recognize what their mind and body are actually doing.

I have spent many hours coaching clients with high blood pressure and teaching them to normalize with nothing but their breath. One client told me, "You have helped me more than 33 cardiologists and all my years in Sunday school!"

All I did was teach her how to exhale -- no drugs, no lectures on how to think more positively. Just breathing. Just letting it all go.

Chapter 5:
Eight Minutes to Inner Peace Exercise Three: Circular Breathing Makes You Feel Happy

"Controlling the breath, and thus claiming the nerves, is a prerequisite to controlling the mind and the body."

\- *Swami Rama*

Here's how to practice circular breathing:

1. Either sit up straight with your chest spread, or lie comfortably.
2. If you are sitting down, make sure you press your shoulders back and lift the tip of your sternum so that your lungs can expand completely.
3. If you are lying down, make sure you are on your back with your chest spread and your lungs open.
4. Place your hands on your belly.
5. As you inhale, feel your belly and rib cage expand and your chest widen.
6. If it's helpful, keep one hand on your belly, and allow the other hand to alternate between your rib cage and upper chest.

7. As you exhale, feel your belly contract and fall back toward your spine.
8. Notice how there is a natural pause at the top and the bottom of your inhale.
9. Set your intention to create an equal length of inhale and exhale so that you spend as much time breathing in as you do breathing out.
10. Relax and enjoy the way you feel!

One of the quickest ways to feel happy is through the pranayama technique called circular breathing.

When you equalize the lengths of your inhale and exhale, you balance the sympathetic and parasympathetic sides of your nervous system.

When I sat for years with my biofeedback device from the Institute of HeartMath, I noticed most people breathe in a fragmented fashion. The failure to take complete inhales and fully let go with the exhales leads to incoherence in their EKGs.

According to scientific research, feelings of anger, worry and frustration create incoherent patterns in your EKG while feelings of love, care and appreciation create a state of coherence.

When your EKG returns to coherence, the rhythm looks like a beautiful sine wave with balanced frequency and amplitude, and your EKG entrains your brain waves. Your brain produces its own natural antidepressants, and your body creates dehydroepiandrosterone (DHEA), which is the mother hormone from which all other hormones are made.

Simply put, when your heart goes into coherence, you feel happy and reverse the aging process.

From years of using the HeartMath device, I learned the fastest way to bring your heart rhythm into coherence is with circular breathing.

At rest, the average adult breathes 12 to 15 times per minute. As you practice circular breathing, you'll notice your respiratory rate will slow down. You may inhale and exhale so completely that you take as few as six breaths per minute.

Yes, you take fewer breaths, but the entire experience is longer, smoother, deeper and fuller, expanding your lung capacity and increasing the oxygen and energy available to your brain and every cell of your body.

One other note: When we're tense, the diaphragm muscles contract, cutting off awareness of our lower body. Slow, deep, circular breaths allow us to reconnect our mind and body, bringing our awareness fully into the present where all joy is actually experienced.

Chapter 6: Eight Minutes to Inner Peace Exercise Four: Clear Your Emotional Body with Bellows Breath

"Feelings come and go like clouds in a windy sky. Conscious breathing is my anchor."

- *Thich Nhat Hanh*

Here's how to practice Bellows Breath:

1. If you have been lying down, sit up.
2. Make sure you press your shoulders back and lift the tip of your sternum so that your lungs can expand completely.
3. Keeping your mouth closed, rapidly breathe out as you contract your solar plexus in a strong, regular pumping motion.
4. Take about one breath per second.
5. Your inhale will naturally occur in the pause of your breath.
6. Whenever you feel tired, pause and take a natural breath.
7. Then resume Bellows Breath.
8. Relax and enjoy the way you feel!

Bellows Breath, or Bhastrika pranayama as we call it in yoga, will allow you to clear your emotional body.

Clearing your emotions is one of the most important things you can ever do for your overall health. They can shut down the functioning of literally any of your really important parts -- your organs, muscles, digestion and even your ability to think straight.

How can Bellows Breath be so effective? When you practice it, you breathe in and out of your third chakra.

The third chakra, or solar plexus center, is your hub for psychic feeling. It's the place where you process emotions -- your own feelings as well as those you pick up from other people.

Many people feel anxious, fatigued or even depressed as a result of picking up energy and emotions from everyone around them. They may even be unclear about which emotions are original and which feelings started with someone else.

Some people are "empaths" with a subconscious ability to process other people's energy, feelings and emotions.

You may be able to get away with sensing other people's emotional states as long as everybody around you happens to feel happy. However, this ability can turn into a liability when you become energetically enmeshed in tragedy, anxiety or other distressing energies.

Processing other people's energy is a huge, hidden cause of much anxiety and depression.

During my medical intuitive readings, I've found that being affected by other people's feelings also can lead to intestinal problems, as congested emotional energy in the third chakra can shut down your digestive process.

Although we all have emotions, many of the feelings we experience aren't actually ours. They're just frequencies we have gone into sympathetic resonance with as a result of spending time with other people.

Many times we pick up energy and emotions from other people without understanding exactly what they are or why we're resonating with the feelings.

Bellows Breath allows you to clear out whatever emotions you're processing – yours, mine or ours -- so you can begin operating again, sparkling and refreshed, from your own center of focus.

With the power to clear away our emotional garbage, Bellows Breath is a stress management tool that doesn't take very much time to be highly effective.

If you rank your stress level before you begin Bellows Breath -- say a 7 out of 10 -- you'll notice you can reduce your feelings of anxiety very quickly.

From a physiological viewpoint, Bellows Breath also tones your diaphragm muscles.

Many people live primarily in their heads and are cut off from their lower body.

Bellows Breath allows you to reconnect with your entire self and feel more emotionally stable, grounded and at peace with all of who you are.

Healing happens when we learn to breathe through what happens in our lives, knowing and experiencing that we are strong enough to handle whatever God has thrown at us.

Chapter 7: Eight Minutes to Inner Peace Exercise Five: Build Your Endurance with Breath of Fire

"Unexpressed emotions will never die. They are buried alive and will come forth later in uglier ways."

- *Sigmund Freud*

Here's how to practice Breath of Fire:

1. If you have been lying down, sit up.
2. Make sure you press your shoulders back and lift the tip of your sternum so that your lungs can expand completely.
3. While keeping your mouth closed, rapidly breathe out as you contract your solar plexus in a strong, regular pumping motion.
4. Your inhale will naturally occur in the pause of your breath.
5. Although Breath of Fire is similar in action to Bellows Breath, which occurs at about one breath per second, Breath of Fire is even more rapid at about two to three cycles per second.
6. Whenever you feel tired, pause and

take a natural breath.
7. Then resume Breath of Fire.
8. Relax and enjoy the way you feel!

You can build your endurance and quickly release a tremendous amount of repressed emotional material with Breath of Fire. It allows you to reconnect with your lower body, which often gets disconnected in our highly mental society. It tones your adrenal glands, builds endurance, stimulates the sympathetic side of your nervous system and expands your energy.

Like Bellows Breath, Breath of Fire allows you to move quickly through the suppressed emotions lying beneath the surface of your conscious awareness.

You hold your emotions not just in your mind but in every cell of your body. In fact, you tend to hold different emotions in specific areas of your body.

When I'm doing a medical intuitive reading, I determine which emotions have caused you to become sick, which feelings you are still holding in specific organs, and what you can do to release the old feelings that are making you ill.

If you think of the old traumas as simply stuck energy, you can begin to comprehend how powerful Breath of Fire can be in releasing post-traumatic stress disorder (PTSD).

You breathe so rapidly that you fully oxygenate your body, mobilizing the stuck energy so efficiently that you often don't even realize which traumas you're releasing.

Although you may have been aware that you're feeling angry, upset, anxious or unhappy, you may not always be able to pinpoint or even verbalize just exactly why.

Breath of Fire allows you to clear the old emotions without needing to talk about them, identify the cause or understand what has been bothering you.

As a result, I find the technique to be highly effective for helping to resolve emotional upsets that occurred before a person was old enough to understand what was happening.

You also can turn to Breath of Fire for traumas that feel so overwhelming you can't even begin to discuss them. Or you can use the technique whenever you want to feel better and really don’t want to talk about what happened.

Human beings have remarkable resilience, and yet the truth is that much of what we experience goes past what tender hearts can handle.

Breath of Fire stimulates your solar plexus -- your center for psychic feeling -- and allows you to clear whatever emotions are lying just on the surface of your mind.

Even if you feel tired during the rapid breathing, you’ll be more energized and psychically clear when you’re done.

Alternate Nostril Breathing

Chapter 8: Eight Minutes to Inner Peace Exercise Six: Balance Your Brain with Alternate Nostril Breathing

"Happiness is not a matter of intensity but of balance, order, rhythm and harmony."

- Thomas Merton

Here's how to practice alternate nostril breathing:

1. If you have been lying down, sit up.
2. If either side of your nose feels congested, take a tissue and blow your nose until both sides feel clearer.
3. Make sure you press your shoulders back and lift the tip of your sternum so that your lungs can expand completely.
4. With your right hand, fold your pointer and middle fingers toward the palm of your hand.
5. With your left hand, bring your thumb together with your pointer and middle fingers.
6. Place the thumb of your right hand on the right side of your nose and the ring finger of your right hand on the left

side of your nose.

7. As you inhale, your thumb closes your right nostril.
8. Exhale through your left nostril.
9. Inhale and close your left nostril with your right ring finger.
10. Take your thumb off your nostril. Exhale through your right nostril.
11. Repeat the cycle.
12. Relax and enjoy the way you feel!

Alternate nostril breathing, also called Nadi Shodhana in the yoga tradition, is one of the most powerful yoga breathing techniques at your disposal. It will stop a panic attack, calm anxiety and allow you to balance your right and left hemispheres, giving you full access to your brain's potential.

Here's a great story about alternate nostril breathing.

One of my long-term yoga students went to the bank one day. Somehow or another, the bank made a massive mistake, and thousands of dollars had suddenly disappeared from an account my student managed for her family farm.

There was nothing my student could do in the

moment except to get a hold of her own emotions.

As thoughts flashed through her mind about having to explain to each relative how the bank had lost their money, she started practicing alternate nostril breathing.

She stopped her own panic attack in its tracks.

Students also find this breathing technique useful before a big test because it integrates the nondominant side of the brain, allowing them to see the big picture and also have access to the details.

Alternate nostril breathing is a powerful technique for balancing not only your nervous system but also your endocrine glands. As you press your fingers into an acupressure point on the corner of your nose, you balance the pituitary gland, which in turn governs your thyroid and adrenal glands.

Although this breathing exercise is number six in the Eight Minutes to Inner Peace routine, it's one of the most powerful for changing your state of mind when you have as little as two minutes to feel better.

I like this tool so much because, like my yoga student at the bank, we very often find ourselves in situations where there's only you, your body and your breath.

In yogic tradition, the two main energy channels on either side of the spine are the ida and pingala, which we discussed in Book 1, Chapter 12. As you practice alternate nostril breathing, you're balancing those two channels, therefore balancing your own life force, your own male and female energies, your own yin and yang chi.

Bumblebee Breath

Chapter 9:
Eight Minutes to Inner Peace Exercise Seven: Clear Your Mind with Bumblebee Breath

"The universe is conscious, breathing and live. Want proof? Look in the mirror!"
- *Tui Sigman*

Here's how to perform Bumblebee Breath:

1. If you have been lying down, sit up.
2. Make sure you press your shoulders back and lift the tip of your sternum so that your lungs can expand completely.
3. One unique feature of Bumblebee Breath is the mudra, or hand position, used to activate it. The specific mudra used in Bumblebee Breath is called Shanmukhi Mudra.
4. Place your thumbs in your ears and gently close your earflaps.
5. Close your eyelids and gently place your ring finger on your closed eyes.
6. Spread your pointer and middle fingers in a V position around the middle of your forehead to frame your sixth chakra (or third eye).

7. Gently rest your little fingers on each cheekbone. Although it may feel a bit awkward at first to close your eyes and ears and place your fingers as directed, you will find yourself feeling deeply connected with your higher self.
8. Then close your lips and make a deep humming sound like a bumblebee. It's OK if you laugh the first time you try -- I certainly did!
9. When you get to the end of your hum and feel like you need some oxygen, take a breath and then repeat.
10. When you begin to practice Bumblebee Breath, start with three to five repetitions, and move up to no more than 17 times per sitting.
11. Relax and enjoy the way you feel!

My absolute favorite yoga breathing technique of all time is Bhramari (pronounced BRUM-er-ee) pranayama -- also known as Bumblebee Breath.

If you have ever tried to meditate only to be disturbed by the relentless flow of thoughts through your mind, you will appreciate the energetic effects of this pranayama technique.

Bumblebee Breath clears your mind in 60

seconds. Literally!

Scientists have discovered a mysterious humming at the center of the Milky Way galaxy that apparently sounds very much like Bumblebee Breath.

Although all pranayama techniques connect your mind with your body, Bumblebee Breath creates a deep feeling of inner stillness while, at the same time, helping you to feel connected to the entire universe.

Other benefits you may experience:

- Natural healing remedy for anxiety
- Natural healing remedy for headaches
- Natural healing remedy for insomnia
- Natural healing remedy for stress
- Natural healing remedy for obsessive compulsive disorder

As you finish, notice how the chatter in your mind has ceased.

Enjoy the peace within!

Chapter 10:
Eight Minutes to Inner Peace
Exercise Eight: Access Your Inner Power and Serenity with Ocean Breath

"Imagine that each time you inhale that the universe is breathing into you and as you exhale it is breathing out of you."

- *Andrew Weil*

Here's how to practice Ocean Breath:

1. Either sit up straight with your chest spread, or lie comfortably.
2. If you are sitting down, make sure you press your shoulders back and lift the tip of your sternum so that your lungs can expand completely.
3. If you are lying down, make sure you are on your back with your chest spread and your lungs open.
4. Open your mouth and exhale as you make the sound of the ocean at the back of your throat.
5. Inhale while continuing to make the ocean sound.

6. Close your lips gently, and continue making the ocean sound.
7. Repeat the cycle with your lips closed, breathing in and out of your nose as you make the ocean sound at the back of your throat.
8. Relax and enjoy the way you feel!

You can access your inner power and serenity with Ocean Breath.

While it's the final breathing or pranayama technique in the Eight Minutes routine, it's often the first breathing pattern new students learn in introductory yoga classes.

I remember when I first learned Ocean Breath, also called Ujayii or Victorious Breath. I felt powerful, calm and energized all at the same time!

My most remarkable story about Ocean Breath involves weight loss. I explained to a new yoga class that Ocean Breath increases metabolism and qualifies as a truly aerobic exercise because it brings oxygen to every cell in the body.

One of the 22 students in that class was listening very carefully. She started practicing

Ocean Breath all day long -- every hour she was awake.

The student came to yoga class only once a week and practiced no other formal exercise. Yet she managed to lose 22 pounds without any dietary changes.

Ocean Breath's benefits:

- Balances blood pressure
- Calms anxiety
- Alleviates depression
- Connects your mind and body
- Increases metabolism
- Allows you to perform great athletic deeds with poise and grace
- Heals asthma and other breathing difficulties
- Balances your sympathetic and parasympathetic nervous systems
- Accesses unlimited energy now

Even if you aren't a yogi, you'll enjoy practicing this breathing technique every time you exercise. You'll find yourself enjoying your workouts even more and feeling more energized afterwards.

Ocean Breath allows you to fill your full lung

capacity. That's why I recommend you finish your breathwork routine with this technique.

You can access unlimited energy but also maintain the inner peace your breathwork practice has created.

Chapter 11: On Vacation with a Mass Murderer

"I am learning to love the sound of my feet walking away from things not meant for me."

- Yash Bhatt

All of my directions and encouragement about how to breathe may seem pretty academic and possibly not even relevant to you, so let me give you a real-life story from one of my clients, a software developer who commuted to Atlanta for work.

I hadn't seen the gentleman in about three months. He had been on vacation.

When he came back, I noticed he was hardly breathing. Like barely at all.

Like he was actually holding his breath.

"How could this be?" I wondered (and worried).

Before he went on his trip, we had discussed how much he needed to take time off to recover from adrenal burnout. He knew he felt terribly exhausted and overworked, so he scheduled the time off to hang out at his home in the Washington, D.C., suburbs.

Only problem: About the same time my student went on vacation, a mass murderer was on the loose.

People would go to their nearest Home Depot, hoping to pick up a few plumbing supplies, only to get shot dead in the parking lot. Some of the violence occurred about a half mile from where my client lived.

How easily can you recover from stress if you don't feel safe?

How can you recover from anxiety when what's happening around you is so life-threatening?

When my student returned to Atlanta from his ineffective vacation, his breathing was so stuck that I encouraged him to lie on his belly.

Now you may not be vacationing with a mass murderer, but there are times when the stress in your life may feel so utterly ridiculous that you can't seem to get away from it.

Here's what to do when you're so stressed that you notice you tend to hold your breath:

Lie on your belly and turn your head to one side.

When you were an infant, your mother may have lay you down this way to calm you and stop your crying. This position is truly soothing and helps you to feel reconnected to the earth, your body and your heartbeat.

As you lie on the floor, your diaphragm muscle pushes into the ground to help bring your breath deep into your belly.

When you tend to hold your breath, you may notice you're breathing primarily out of your upper chest, which keeps you stuck in the fight-or-flight part of your nervous system.

When that happens, your body will be constantly pushing out two highly destructive stress hormones, cortisol and adrenalin. They quite literally break down everything important in your body -- brain chemistry, your hair, even your bones.

When you hold your breath, you may notice you feel tired but wired.

Breathing while lying on your belly with your head turned to the side balances the acupuncture meridian for your spleen, which gets especially stressed when you worry.

If all else fails and the fancy breathing exercises feel like too much for you, lie on the floor and rely on belly breathing, allowing the trauma to fall away with each breath.

BOOK IV

16 Simple Mudras to Activate Divine Energy

Chapter 1: How Do Yoga Mudras Actually Work?

"Most men pursue pleasure with such breathless haste that they hurry past it."
- Soren Kierkegaard

Although breathing exercises alone will bless you in multiple ways, you can exponentially increase the benefit of your practice by incorporating simple hand gestures called mudras.

One of the simplest ways to begin to shift your energy toward greater vitality and health is to take advantage of the science of yoga mudras.

What are yoga mudras? They are symbols you create with your hands. They're included in the ancient science of yoga, but you don't have to practice the physical postures, asanas or breathing exercises called pranayama to take advantage of the magic of mudras.

Traditionally, you hold your fingers and hands in specific positions to connect certain energy flows in your mind-body system.

In this book, we're focusing on 16 simple mudras you can use anytime and anywhere in conjunction with the breathing exercises.

If you'd like to learn more, I have put together a series of videos of 33 yoga mudras that you can learn for FREE at the following link: https://unlimitedenergynow.com/yoga-mudras

So how do yoga mudras work? Based on my 24 years of teaching and practicing yoga, here is my best explanation:

1. Mudras alter the flow of energy through your acupuncture system. All your acupuncture meridians either begin or end in your hands or feet. When you change the position of your hands and fingers, you literally alter the prana in your body. You can think of it as rewiring the subtle currents.
2. Your thumbs activate your lung meridian.
3. Your pointer fingers activate your large intestine meridian.
4. Your middle fingers activate your circulation sex meridian.
5. Your ring fingers activate your triple warmer meridian.

6. Your little fingers activate both your heart and small intestine meridians.
7. In addition to activating the acupuncture meridians, mudras balance the five elements of fire, air, ether or space, earth and water in your body.
8. Your thumbs activate fire energy.
9. Your pointer fingers activate air.
10. Your middle fingers activate ether or space.
11. Your ring fingers activate earth energy.
12. Your little fingers activate water energy.
13. When you hold your palms up, you call in (or summon) more prana from the universe.
14. When you turn your palms down, you allow yourself to focus on circulating your internal prana.
15. Your energy body, or pranamaya kosha, literally controls your physical body. We've all had the experience of feeling so tired you can hardly move or having so much vitality you seem capable of exceeding your physical boundaries. Your pranamaya kosha includes your acupuncture meridians, your chakras and your breath. As you change the configuration of your hands and fingers, you redirect the flow of

energy through your pranamaya kosha and thereby transform your entire mind-body experience.

16. Because illness occurs as a result of either too much or too little energy in the pranamaya kosha as well as the organs in your body, mudras can be powerful tools for healing. Use these simple, free, drug-free natural healing methods when you want to bring your own prana into balance.
17. By bringing your acupuncture meridians and five elements into energetic alignment, you bring your entire mind-body system into balance, thereby energizing your entire being and blessing yourself with fabulous health. No matter how old or sick you are, you can open yourself to a higher level of prana and heal yourself naturally from the inside out.

Don't believe me? Try this simple experiment.

Take a few breaths. Notice the quality of your breath. Make note of your state of mind.

Now place your thumb and pointer finger together on each hand. Breathe again.

What you'll notice is that just by bringing your thumb and pointer finger together, your breath will drop from your upper chest down into your ribs.

Now bring your thumb together with your pointer finger as well as the middle finger of each hand. Breathe again.

You'll notice that just by holding this new configuration, your breath automatically drops deep into your belly, and you feel even calmer.

Simply by changing the way you hold your hands and your fingers, you can redirect the subtle energies in your body.

You can feel this shift yourself -- just try it!

If I am teaching beginner students how to breathe more deeply, the first thing I will have them do is hold these simple mudras to make the process easier. Stress just begins to melt away.

Each mudra I'm describing for you in this book aligns your energy for a different purpose.

How long do you need to hold a mudra? It depends on the quality of your current energy.

Are you exhausted and depleted? Do you feel anxious and rattled? You would need to hold the mudras long enough to feel the shift.

However, the instant you change the position of your fingers and hands, you begin to alter the flow of energy in your body.

I liken the experience to plugging the cord of an electrical lamp into a socket.

The longer you hold the mudra, the more your energy can flow in a specific direction.

I recommend holding each mudra while practicing the breathing exercises or sitting quietly in meditation.

Make note of your state of mind before and afterwards.

As you learn the mudras, however, you can practice them even when you aren't closing your eyes to meditate. You can practice them anywhere and anytime you need to call on your own inner strength.

I like mudras' natural healing remedies because I'm often working with people who don't have the money for herbs, flower essences, supplements or outside practitioners.

If all you have is yourself, you can learn these simple tools and rest assured you are blessing yourself with powerful medicine.

Healing happens when we take advantage of natural healing remedies like mudras, which cost no money, can be performed anytime and anywhere by anybody and need no equipment.

Anjali Mudra, Divinity

Chapter 2: Anjali Mudra, Divinity

"My home is in heaven. I'm just traveling through this world."
- *Billy Graham*

You can greet others with Anjali Mudra or hold your hands together in this way to demonstrate how much you honor and respect them.

Here's how to perform this mudra:

1. Bring your palms together at your heart.
2. As you bring your palms together, silently salute the divine within you by honoring the divine within everyone. That is the meaning of the salutation "namaste."

You can also hold Anjali as you pray.

As you are holding this mudra, you may want to repeat these affirmations:

I HONOR THE DIVINE
WITHIN ME.
I HONOR THE
DIVINITY OF OTHERS.
THE DIVINE WITHIN ME HONORS THE
DIVINE WITHIN YOU.
I ALLOW DIVINE ENERGY TO FLOW
THROUGH ME FOR THE BENEFIT OF
ALL LIVING BEINGS.
I ALIGN MY WILL
WITH GOD'S WILL.
I AM ONE WITH THE BLESSINGS OF
THE UNIVERSE.
I EXPERIENCE MY DIVINITY
EXPRESSING ITSELF THROUGH
MY HUMANITY.
I ALLOW DIVINE GRACE TO FLOW
THROUGH ME AND TO ME.
I AM HUMBLE BEFORE THE BEAUTY
AND WONDER OF THE UNIVERSE.
I AM AT ONE WITH ALL THAT IS.

Apana Mudra, Purification

Chapter 3: Apana Mudra, Purification

"Purify yourself from the attributes of self so that you may see your own pure, untarnished essence."

- Rumi

Apana Mudra is the hand gesture you turn to for purification.

Whether you are wanting to detoxify your internal organs or cleanse your mind of unwanted thoughts, Apana Mudra will clear the space.

To perform this mudra:

1. Bring the thumb of each hand together with your middle and ring fingers.
2. Extend the other fingers.

As you perform Apana Mudra, use these affirmations:

I NOW CLEANSE MY BODY, MIND AND SPIRIT OF ALL ENERGIES THAT NO LONGER SERVE FOR MY HIGHEST GOOD.

I GROUND MY ENERGY TO THE
EARTH.
I AM PATIENT, SERENE, CONFIDENT
AND IN HARMONY WITH THE WORLD
AROUND ME.
I CLEAR MY ENERGY IN THE NAME OF
GOD THE FATHER, JESUS THE SON
AND OF THE HOLY GHOST,
MY INNER AND OUTER CLARITY
CONTRIBUTES TO MY INCREASED
SPIRITUAL DISCERNMENT.
I JOYFULLY RELEASE ALL I NO
LONGER NEED.
I KEEP MY VIBRATION CLEAR AND
OPEN FOR THE HIGHEST GOOD.
I LET GO AND LET GOD.

Bhutadamar Mudra, Protection

Chapter 4: Bhutadamar Mudra, Protection

"What matters most is how well you walk through the fire."
- Charles Bukowski

There are times in life when you feel overwhelmed by negativity.

You may find yourself surrounded by the negative emotions of others -- anger, fear, shame, blame, guilt, greed, hysteria, even emotional or physical violence.

Or you could find yourself the target of a personal attack.

Many highly sensitive people may be so empathic that they pick up negative energy not only immediately surrounding them but in faraway places -- war, global conflicts and threats to the environment over which they have no actual control.

You may have no good methods to keep yourself from being affected by the negative energy and find yourself feeling anxious, depressed or overwhelmed.

One of the most powerful ways you can stay in your calm, peaceful center is to activate Bhutadamar Mudra, a shield against negative energies.

Here's how to activate Bhutadamar Mudra:

1. Turn your palms facing away from your body.
2. Fold your ring finger down toward your palm.
3. Cross your arms.
4. Bring your awareness to the sound of your breath.
5. Visualize yourself surrounded by the white light of protection.
6. Rest in your center as long as you like, rediscovering the peace within yourself.

Bhutadamar Mudra turns on the energy of your ring finger, which corresponds to the earth element. Your ring finger activates your root or Muladhara chakra. By energizing your root chakra, you feel grounded, courageous and confident.

Bhutadamar Mudra may be an essential survival skill for highly sensitive people.

If you know you are an empath, I recommend

practicing this mudra first thing in the morning, anytime you feel your own inner peace has been disrupted and again before you go to sleep.

While you practice Bhutadamar Mudra, use these affirmations:

NOTHING COMES IN AND NOTHING GOES OUT EXCEPT UNCONDITIONAL LOVE.
I AM GUIDED AND PROTECTED AT ALL TIMES AND IN ALL PLACES.
THE LIGHT OF GOD SURROUNDS ME.
THE LOVE OF GOD PROTECTS ME.
I AM SAFE.
I AM SURROUNDED BY DIVINE ENERGY NOW.
I AM LIFTED UP BY THE LOVE OF GOD.
I EXPERIENCE THE SAFETY OF BEING MY TRUE SELF.

Chin Mudra, Integration

Chapter 5: Chin Mudra, Integration

"Deep breathing brings deep thinking, and shallow breathing brings shallow thinking."
- Elsie Lincoln Benedict

One of the most commonly used mudras is Chin Mudra. You can use this mudra anytime you want to experience greater integration of body, mind and spirit.

As you draw your awareness inside, you create the space to process all your life's experiences. You shut yourself off from receiving additional information and allow your soul to integrate what's been happening.

Here's how to activate Chin Mudra:

1. Bring your thumb and pointer finger together.
2. Extend the other three fingers.
3. Turn your palms down toward the earth. As you do so, draw your awareness inside.

This mudra appears similar to Jnana Mudra, in which your fingers hold a similar position but your palms turn up toward the heavens. By turning your palms down in Chin Mudra, you put yourself in a mode to assimilate what you have already received.

As you activate Chin Mudra, you may want to use these affirmations:

MY MIND, BODY AND SPIRIT COME
INTO HARMONY NOW.
I EXPERIENCE DIVINE INTEGRATION.
I INTEGRATE MY MIND,
BODY AND SPIRIT.
I ACCESS THE WISDOM WITHIN.
ALL I NEED TO KNOW COMES
TO ME EASILY BY GRACE
IN DIVINE TIMING.
I AM DIVINELY GUIDED
FROM WITHIN.
MY TRUE SELF LEADS THE WAY.
I AWAKEN MY AWARENESS OF MY
DIVINE CONNECTION.

Dhyana Mudra, Serenity

Chapter 6: Dhyana Mudra, Serenity

"I meet my Self in stillness, and we breathe."
- *S.W. Berry*

Dhyana Mudra shifts your mind, body and spirit into a state of deep inner peace.

If you're preparing to meditate or simply want to calm your nerves anytime anywhere, Dhyana Mudra is the hand position to turn to for instant centering.

This mudra is a natural healing remedy for anxiety. What's so great is that you can let go of your stress naturally -- no drugs, no therapist required!

Here's how to activate Dhyana Mudra:

1. Sit in a comfortable position. Lengthen your spine to make space for your lungs to breathe fully.
2. Bring your left hand into your lap.
3. Rest your right hand on top of your left hand.
4. Bring your thumbs together.
5. Relax completely.

As you sit with your hands in Dhyana Mudra, feel your energy gradually coming into perfect alignment.

Your breath slows down. The clutter of your mind begins to clear. Your energy naturally drops into your center.

Enjoy the restfulness.

As you hold Dhyana Mudra, use these affirmations:

I AM ONE WITH THE DIVINE PRESENCE
WITHIN ME.
I EXPERIENCE PEACE
AND SERENITY.
I AM SERENE.
I AM A LIGHT OF GOD'S
LOVE WHEREVER I GO,
WHOMEVER I AM WITH.
I AM THE LIGHT.
I LIVE IN THE LIGHT.
I CHOOSE TO CHANNEL THE HIGHEST
VIBRATIONS FOR THE HIGHEST GOOD
OF ALL.
I AM AT PEACE.

Jnana Mudra, Knowledge

Chapter 7: Jnana Mudra, Knowledge

"If you want to conquer the anxiety of life, live in the moment, live in the breath."
- *Amrit Ray*

Jnana Mudra is the hand gesture to turn to whenever you seek inspiration, guidance, understanding and wisdom.

Here's how to perform Jnana Mudra:

1. Bring the thumb of each hand together with your pointer finger.
2. Turn your palms upward.

Although this mudra appears similar to Chin Mudra, in which your fingers hold a similar position but your palms turn toward the earth, you put yourself in a receptive mode by turning your palms upward in Jnana Mudra.

You can use the following affirmations with Jnana Mudra:

I NOW KNOW WHAT I NEED TO KNOW
WHEN I NEED TO KNOW IT.
KNOWLEDGE AND WISDOM

FLOW TO ME NOW BY
GRACE IN DIVINE TIMING.
I OPEN MYSELF TO
DIVINE GUIDANCE.
I SHOW UP AND GET MY
EGO OUT OF THE WAY.
I ALLOW MYSELF TO BE
DIVINELY GUIDED.
THE WISDOM OF GOD FLOWS
THROUGH ME FOR THE
HIGHEST GOOD OF ALL.

Kapitthaka Mudra, Happiness

Chapter 8: Kapitthaka Mudra, Happiness

"If you want others to be happy, practice compassion. If you want to be happy, practice compassion."

- *Dalai Lama*

Use Kapitthaka Mudra whenever you want to experience happiness.

Here's how to perform Kapitthaka Mudra:

1. Tuck your ring and little fingers down inside your palm.
2. Bring your thumbs on top of your ring and little fingers.
3. Bring your index and middle fingers together and point each hand upward.

As you breathe and discover your bliss body, happiness naturally arises. Holding Kapitthaka Mudra can amplify this feeling of quiet joy.

Use these affirmations as you hold Kapitthaka Mudra:

I AM HAPPY INSIDE AND OUT.
HAPPINESS FLOWS THROUGH ME.
I AM A DIVINE CHANNEL FOR
THE JOY OF LIFE.
I FEEL SO HAPPY!
I NATURALLY UPLIFT EVERYONE
AROUND ME.
LIFE IS FUN AND EASY FOR ME.
I EXPERIENCE DIVINE DELIGHT.
I KNOW HOW TO BE HAPPY.
IT'S EASY FOR ME TO FEEL HAPPY.
HAPPINESS IS MY BIRTHRIGHT.

Kubera Mudra, Abundance

Chapter 9: Kubera Mudra, Abundance

"The universe provides abundantly when you're in a state of gratefulness."
- *Wayne Dyer*

One of the most important ways to manifest anything you want is to put yourself in the frequency of what you choose to be, do or have.

For example, if you want to look more beautiful, then *feel* more beautiful. You can't change how you look on your outside until you change what's really going on inside.

If you want to make more money, think like the most financially wise people you know.

If you want to earn a higher income, act like the people you know who earn more. Do they make wiser choices when they spend, do they exercise the self-discipline to save -- what exactly do they do that you aren't currently doing?

To have what you want, ask yourself, "What do I need to be or do differently?" You can't remain the way you are and achieve something different -- you literally have to shift both inside and out.

Kubera Mudra is a yoga hand position traditionally used to access this frequency of success and abundance.

Here's how to perform Kubera Mudra:

1. Fold your little finger and ring finger into the palm of each hand.
2. Bring your pointer and middle fingers together with your thumb.
3. Rest your hands in the palm of your lap.
4. Relax, meditate and breathe!

While you are holding Kubera Mudra, use these affirmations:

GOD IS MY SUPPLY AND MY SUPPORT.
THE WORLD I EXPERIENCE IS THE RESULT OF THE PICTURE WITHIN MY MIND.
I NOW SEE THE DIVINE ABUNDANCE THAT IS MY BIRTHRIGHT.
I PARTICIPATE IN THE ABUNDANCE OF THE BEAUTY AND WONDER OF THE UNIVERSE.

I PARTICIPATE IN PLENTY.
I EXPRESS THE TRUE NATURE
OF ABUNDANCE.
I CHANNEL THE FREQUENCY
OF ABUNDANCE.
I HAVE COMPLETED THE CYCLE OF
CONTRACTING AND NOW EXPAND MY
CAPACITY
TO GIVE AND RECEIVE.
I LET GO AND ALLOW GOD TO
PROVIDE FOR ME.
I FEEL TRULY GRATEFUL AND
EXPRESS MY GRATITUDE IN EVER-
EXPANDING WAYS.
I ALLOW MY DIVINE SPIRIT TO
LEAD ME TO WONDERFUL
OPPORTUNITIES NOW.
I PLAN FOR SUCCESS.
I APPRECIATE ALL MY LIFE'S
BLESSINGS AND GIVE THANKS FOR
ALL I RECEIVE.

Linga Mudra, Immunity

Chapter 10: Linga Mudra, Immunity

"It's not the load that breaks you down, it's the way you carry it."

- Lou Holtz

Use Linga Mudra whenever you want to strengthen your immune system.

Because stress and tension quite literally make us sick, if you find yourself under the weather, you can turn to this mudra to rebuild the energy in your immune system.

Linga Mudra is especially helpful for the lungs and guards against colds and cold weather.

Here's how to perform Linga Mudra:

1. Interlace your fingers.
2. Point one thumb upward.
3. Encircle your extended thumb with the opposite thumb and index finger.

As you hold Linga Mudra, you can use these affirmations:

EVERY DAY IN EVERY WAY I AM BECOMING HEALTHIER AND HEALTHIER.
MY LUNGS ARE STRONG AND HEALTHY.
NOTHING COMES IN AND NOTHING GOES OUT EXCEPT UNCONDITIONAL LOVE.
I BREATHE IN ALL THAT HEALS ME.
I BREATHE OUT ALL THAT NO LONGER SERVES ME.
I ENJOY A STRONG, HEALTHY IMMUNE SYSTEM.
I FEEL THE DIVINE PRESENCE WITHIN, CREATING PERFECT HEALTH INSIDE AND OUT.

Mantangi Mudra, Peace

Chapter 11: Mantangi Mudra, Peace

"Imagine all the people living life in peace. You may say I'm a dreamer, but I'm not the only one. I hope someday you'll join us, and the world will be as one."

- John Lennon

Access the frequency of Mantangi Mudra whenever you want to experience deep inner peace.

Here's how to perform Mantangi Mudra:

1. Interlace the fingers of both hands.
2. Bring your middle fingers together in a steeple position.
3. Extend both fingers upward toward the sky.

As you hold your hands in Mantangi Mudra, affirm:

I NOW REST IN THE PEACE THAT
SURPASSES ALL UNDERSTANDING.
MY MIND IS AT PEACE.
WHEN I VIEW THE WORLD AROUND
ME, I WITNESS THE PEACE AND

PERFECTION THAT GOD
HAS ALREADY CREATED.
MY MIND, BODY AND SPIRIT
ARE NOW AT PEACE.
I ALLOW PEACE TO CREATE
HARMONY IN MY MIND,
BODY AND SPIRIT.
I AM AT PEACE WITH THE
WORLD AROUND ME.

Mukula Mudra, Unfoldment

Chapter 12: Mukula Mudra, Unfoldment

"When you arise in the morning, think of what a precious privilege it is to be alive -- to breathe, to think, to enjoy, to love."

\- *Marcus Aurelius*

When you are starting a new job, a new relationship, or a new year at school or want to bring in a fresh perspective, use Mukula Mudra.

This mudra resembles the bud of a flower before it unfolds.

How you perform Mukula Mudra:

1. Bring the fingers of each hand together with your thumb in the shape of a flower bud.
2. Point your palms upward.
3. As you hold Mukula Mudra, notice the blessings that are naturally coming into your life.

While holding Mukula Mudra, use these affirmations:

I ALLOW FRESH ENERGY
INTO MY LIFE.
I AM POSSIBLE.
I AM READY FOR MIRACLES.
I ALLOW MY LIFE TO UNFOLD BY
GRACE IN PERFECT TIMING.
I AM READY FOR THE DIVINE
UNFOLDMENT OF MY LIFE.
I TRUST MY PROCESS.
I ENJOY THE BLESSINGS OF LIFE.
MY GRATITUDE CREATES NEW
OPPORTUNITIES.
I WELCOME BENEFICIAL CHANGE.

Mushti Mudra, Release

Chapter 13: Mushti Mudra, Release

"Although the world is full of suffering, it is also full of the overcoming of it."

- Helen Keller

As we follow the 10 principles of breathwork and begin to release the traumas held way down deep at the cellular level, pent-up emotions may rise to our conscious awareness. It may take tremendous strength to breathe through your emotions.

This mudra makes it easier for you to release whatever has been holding you back.

How to perform Mushti Mudra:

1. Place your thumb over your ring finger.
2. Wrap your other fingers together in a fist on top.
3. Breathe through your feelings as they arise, knowing and experiencing that you are strong enough to let go of these pent-up energies.

As you hold Mushti Mudra, you may want to use the following affirmations:

I AM STRONG ENOUGH TO FEEL
MY FEELINGS.
I AM STRONG ENOUGH TO LET GO OF
THE TRAUMA THAT NO
LONGER SERVES ME.
I LET GO OF THE STORIES THAT HAVE
HELD ME BACK IN THE PAST.
I AM FREE.
I RELEASE THE PAST AND
FORGET IT.
I FORGIVE ALL PAST EXPERIENCES.
I FORGIVE MYSELF
AND EVERYONE.
I LET GO OF MY VICTIM-
PERPETRATOR STORY.
I HAVE COMPLETED THE CYCLE OF
SEEING MYSELF AS A VICTIM AND
NOW TAKE RESPONSIBILITY
FOR ALL I CREATE.
AS I BREATHE, I CLEAR THE SPACE TO
EXPERIENCE PEACE WITHIN.
I PUT THE ENERGY OF MY EMOTIONS
INTO MOTION AND RELEASE THE
TENSION
WAY DOWN DEEP.
I AM SORRY. PLEASE FORGIVE ME.
THANK YOU. I LOVE YOU.
AS I FORGIVE, I ALLOW MY SPIRIT TO
EXPERIENCE THE PEACE THAT
SURPASSES ALL UNDERSTANDING.

If the emotions that rise to the surface feel especially intense, give yourself permission to contain them by either setting a time limit on your breathwork session or visualizing a container that takes in the uncomfortable feelings.

When you reach the end of your time limit or fill your container, get up and shift your energy by doing something different.

Drink a glass of water.

Walk in the sunshine.

Put your energy in motion another way by cleaning out a drawer, completing a work task or finishing a job you have been putting off.

Be kind to yourself, understanding that your soul knows best about when and how to release whatever has been holding you back.

Prana Mudra, Energy

Chapter 14: Prana Mudra, Energy

"I've got to keep breathing. It'll be my worst business mistake if I don't."

- Steve Martin

There are times in life when you simply need more energy to get through the day.

Up at night taking care of a baby.

During a long day at work.

Driving through rush-hour traffic.

When you are so exhausted you can hardly keep your eyes open but life must still go on.

I'm sure you can think of other times and places where just a little more oomph can make all the difference between merely getting by and performing at your very best.

The word prana means energy. The more you have, the better version of you shows up.

Prana has everything to do with your health. When your vitality falls off, you are more susceptible to viruses, bacteria and all manner of illness.

Many people equate good chi with youthfulness, and it's true that when you sparkle with life, you feel young no matter what your age.

The fact is that great prana has nothing to do with your chronological age and everything to do with how well you take care of your body, how well you breathe, how you manage your emotions, how positively you think and how deep your spiritual connection is to all of life.

Having good chi is like having a fat bank account.

You can respond to whatever life throws at you so long as you maintain good prana.

There's no shortage of energy in the universe -- you just have to learn how to do a better job of channeling beneficial energy to nurture yourself on all levels.

We use up energy every day, but the real question becomes how good of a job we do restoring ourselves on all levels.

Use Prana Mudra whenever you need to increase your life energy.

Here's how to activate Prana Mudra:

1. Bring your thumbs together with your ring fingers and little fingers of each hand.
2. Extend your index and middle fingers.
3. Turn the palms up in a receptive position.
4. Visualize yourself receiving beneficial energy from the universe.
5. Feel the prana coming into the palms of your hands and nourishing every cell of your body.
6. Sit quietly while breathing and meditateing.

One reason this mudra works so well is that you take the time to become receptive to the universe's wisdom, support and guidance.

It's important to remember to be yin to become yang.

Yin is the feminine, quiet, inward, still quality.

Yang is masculine, active and outward.

If you study the yin yang symbol, you will notice that the black yin becomes the white yang and vice versa.

If you are constantly active, your body becomes exhausted, and you end up flat on your back.

By stilling your mind with breathwork and practicing Prana Mudra, notice how you naturally restore your energy.

As you hold Prana Mudra, affirm:

I OPENLY AND WILLINGLY RECEIVE
FROM THE UNIVERSE.
I FLOW WITH JOY.
ALL THE ENERGY I NEED TO FEEL
WONDERFUL COMES
EASILY TO ME NOW.
I RECEIVE ALL THE BLESSINGS
OF MY LIFE.
THANK YOU, GOD, FOR BLESSING ME
WITH HEALTH, HAPPINESS
AND VITALITY.
I AM A RECEPTIVE CHANNEL FOR ALL
LIFE'S GOODNESS.
AS I RECEIVE, I AM ABLE TO GIVE AT
HIGHER AND HIGHER LEVELS.

GOD HAS BLESSED ME, AND I NOW
GIVE THANKS FOR ALL I RECEIVE.

Prithivi Mudra, Grounding

Chapter 15: Prithivi Mudra, Grounding

"I'm not crazy about reality but it's still the only place to get a decent meal."

- Groucho Marx

There are times when, as a spiritual person, your energy and attention become so disconnected from your physical body that you become ungrounded. You feel untethered from the earth.

In the extreme, you lose all sense of practicality and feel anxious. You lose your bearings.

You must ground yourself to manifest what you want.

Grounding to the earth gives you stability, support and confidence.

Turn to Prithivi Mudra whenever you need to ground your energy.

Here's how to form the Prithivi Mudra:

1. Bring the tips of your thumbs together

with your ring fingers.
2. Extend your remaining fingers.

As you hold Prithivi Mudra, you may want to affirm:

I AM GROUNDED IN MY BODY
IN THIS LIFETIME.
I LOVE MY BODY.
I GROUND MY ENERGIES TO THE
EARTH AND MANIFEST ALL
I NEED AND WANT.
I ADOPT A PRACTICAL
APPROACH TO LIFE.
I LOVE, HONOR AND CARE
FOR THE EARTH.
FROM MY STRONG AND GROUNDED
ROOTS, I NOW MANIFEST MY
DESTINY.

Ushas Mudra, Creativity

Chapter 16: Ushas Mudra, Creativity

"Be aware of your breathing. Notice how this takes attention away from your thinking and creates space."

- Eckhart Tolle

Use Ushas Mudra when you want to create something new.

Whether you are an artist, writer, singer, dancer, inventor or CEO, honor the way your soul longs to create.

This mudra activates your second chakra, the energy vortex from which your creativity arises.

How to perform Ushas Mudra:

1. Interlace your fingers with your palms facing upward.
2. Place your right thumb on top of your left thumb.

As you hold Ushas Mudra, use these affirmations:

I AM A DIVINE CHANNEL
FOR CREATIVITY.
I ALLOW DIVINE ENERGY TO CREATE
THROUGH ME.
I SET ASIDE MY EGO MIND AND
ALLOW CREATIVITY TO FLOW
THROUGH ME WITH
EASE AND GRACE.
I WELCOME DIVINE INSPIRATION.
I ENJOY CREATING FOR
THE HIGHEST GOOD.
I CREATE SOMETHING GOOD FROM
ALL MY LIFE'S EXPERIENCES.

Uttarabodhi Mudra, Enlightenment

Chapter 17: Uttarabodhi Mudra, Enlightenment

"The point of power is always in the present moment."

- Louise Hay

Uttarabodhi Mudra signifies supreme enlightenment.

As we practice breathwork regularly and begin to feel bliss on a regular basis, we literally raise our vibration. In so doing we have a profound beneficial effect on everyone around us.

The goal of many spiritual seekers is enlightenment.

At this point, while we are meditating or practicing our breathwork, our ego has fallen away not just temporarily but on a constant basis.

Use this mudra when you intend to lift your vibration and experience divine bliss.

How to form Uttarabodhi Mudra:

1. Bring your index fingers together in a steeple position.
2. Cross the remaining fingers.
3. Cross your thumbs.
4. Point your clasped hands toward the sky.

As you hold Uttarabodhi Mudra, you can use these affirmations:

I RAISE MY VIBRATION NOW FOR THE HIGHEST GOOD OF ALL.
I ALLOW THE HIGHEST AND BEST VIBRATIONS TO FLOW THROUGH ME AND TO ME.
I YIELD TO DIVINE WISDOM.
I NOW RELEASE THE GRIP OF MY EGO AND ALLOW MY SOUL TO GUIDE THE WAY.
MY EGO STEPS ASIDE TO MAKE WAY FOR THE DIVINE WISDOM OF MY SOUL.
I SHOW UP AND GET MY EGO OUT OF THE WAY.
I ALIGN MY WILL WITH DIVINE WILL.
I ALLOW GOD TO WORK THROUGH ME IN MYSTERIOUS WAYS.
I AM A CLEAR AND PERFECT CHANNEL FOR DIVINE

LOVE AND LIGHT.
I WELCOME DIVINE LIGHT AND SHINE FORTH FOR THE HIGHEST GOOD OF ALL.

BOOK V

PUTTING WISDOM INTO ACTION

Chapter 1: The Rest of the Story

"In times like these, it's helpful to remember that there have always been times like these."
- Paul Harvey

In my mid-40s, I went for a regular visit to my medical doctor.

As he was going over my intake form, he noticed I had checked the box indicating I had a history of asthma. Later during the same appointment, I found myself breathing into a strange device to measure my lung capacity.

Totally normal. The doctor could find no trace of the asthma.

It had been years since I needed inhalers or allergy shots.

The psychiatric medicine I had been prescribed in the mental hospital had long since been replaced with yoga, breathing exercises, a lower-stress lifestyle and decades of inner work.

I'm not sure exactly when I got over the

asthma.

Nobody hands you a diploma when you can finally breathe normally.

Thankfully, I never had to go back to another mental hospital. Thank God! Once was enough.

Everybody's got a history, but you can't look at a person and tell whether she ever had breathing or emotional problems.

Better not to judge, trusting that people are exactly where they need to be on their spiritual path. And that means you don't need to judge yourself either.

No matter where you are in your life as you read this book, it's all OK.

You just have to keep breathing!

Chapter 2:
Why You, and I Do Mean YOU, Need to Learn How to Breathe

"Just because you're breathing doesn't mean you're alive."
- Epik High Tablo

After reading this book, you may be thinking to yourself, "Well, I've been breathing my whole life. I've gotten this far, haven't I? Why should I bother with any of this?"

Let me explain what happens to your body when you don't take the time to manage your stress.

You get sick. Your job, relationships and life itself feel difficult.

At your lowest points, you wonder how you can make it through another day, another hour, another moment.

Why suffer when you can simply learn how to breathe?

Even if you're not paying much attention, your body provides feedback on how well you're managing your life.

How many of the following symptoms of stress, tension and anxiety do you have right now?

- Increased circulation to your brain and the musculature of your head provides heightened awareness of an emergency situation, which can lead to headaches (even migraines) and possible links to dementia and strokes.
- Your pupils dilate for sharper vision, which can lead to sore, tired eyes and reduced vision over time.
- Your jaws tighten, possibly causing you to grind your teeth and leading to TMJ (dysfunction in your temporo-mandibular joint), eating disorders and oral fixations.
- Your pituitary gland receives messages from the emotional centers of your brain, which can set off a cycle of anxiety, depression and adrenal burnout.
- Your thyroid gland increases metabolism to face a perceived threat. Since your metabolism isn't designed to be elevated on an ongoing basis, this can lead to sleep disorders, chronic fatigue

and reliance on caffeine and nicotine.

- Your thymus gland becomes activated, which ultimately reduces your immune-ity and makes you more vulnerable to viruses and other illnesses.
- Your lungs may hyperventilate to generate rapid short-term energy, which can lead to poor breathing patterns, lack of energy, allergies, colds and coughs as well as chronic lung conditions.
- Your heart and arteries also spring to action when you need a short-term energy supply, increasing your blood pressure and heart rate and possibly leading to high blood pressure, high cholesterol, heart disease, strokes and the hardening of your arteries.
- To mobilize your fight-or-flight response, your adrenal glands produce adrenalin and cortisol, which can lead to adrenal burnout, obesity, low back pain, exhaustion, water retention and hormonal imbalances.
- As part of your defense mechanisms, your back muscles contract, which can lead to muscle spasms as well as chronic neck and back pain.
- To brace for an attack, your discs and vertebrae compress, which can lead to arthritis, joint pain, inflammation and a

wide variety of joint and disc problems in your spine.

- At the same time, the blood in your body likely shifts away from your digestive system to support your large muscles, which can lead to a wide variety of digestive disorders including Crohn's, colitis, IBS, ulcers, diverticulitis, constipation and diarrhea.

If none of the above stress points applies to you, congratulations! You're doing a fabulous job taking care of yourself.

If you placed a checkmark by any of the symptoms above, the simplest, cheapest way to start feeling better in this very moment may be to take up breathwork.

Breathing with full awareness -- even for just a few minutes a couple of times a day -- can radically shift your capacity for handling life.

Chapter 3: Prayer for Inspiration

"Mind is the king of the senses, and the breath is the king of the mind."
- B.K.S. Iyengar

As we come to the end of *The Little Book of Breathwork,* please know that you, my dear readers, will remain in my heart forever. I leave you with this prayer from my heart to your heart.

Heavenly Father,

Thank you for blessing these dear readers
with the knowledge and information
to transform their relationship
with their own breath.
Please bless them with increased energy,
inner peace and the ability to turn
down the volume on the tension
and stress in their lives.
Please inspire them.
Please guide them to the place where they
feel happy inside, knowing and experiencing
how they can create this feeling of lightness,
wisdom and blissful calm anytime anywhere.
Thank you for blessing these dear readers

with lungs to breathe the fresh air.
Thank you for blessing them with the
heart to feel the difference.
Thank you for blessing them with the
willingness to experience health and
happiness in this lifetime.
Thank you God, thank you God,
thank you God.

Amen

Chapter 4: How to Use This Book

"The quality of our breath expresses our inner feelings."
- T.K.V. Desikachar

As you travel throughout the world, you'll find many different systems of natural healing that include breathwork. The yogic practice of pranayama may be the most common.

I am a great believer in creating a practice that works best for you.

Now that you've been introduced to the 10 principles of enlightened breathing, learned the eight specific breathing exercises behind Eight Minutes to Inner Peace and found out about 16 different mudras and affirmations to uplift your mind, you have many choices:

1. Practice Eight Minutes to Inner Peace in its entirety. Boom! You're done. You've made a huge shift in your personal frequency in a very short time period.
2. If there is a health challenge you've been wanting to overcome, focus on the

recommended breathing exercises. Take your time with just one or two techniques.

3. Create a regular breathing routine. Great times to practice are first thing in the morning, to set your vibration at the highest level possible, and again at night to put your mind at rest before going to sleep. In the middle of the day, you can create space for a few minutes of breathwork to nourish your mind and body.
4. If there are particular qualities you want to enhance in your life, use the recommended mudra and the associated affirmations as mantras while you practice your breathing exercises.
5. As you breathe in, repeat the affirmations or series of mantras that feel most helpful for you at this time. As you breathe out, feel the shift inside you.
6. Come up with your own breathwork routine. I love Eight Minutes to Inner Peace, but perhaps another sequence feels and works even better for you.
7. Anytime during the day you need to find a quick burst of energy or shift out of a negative frame of mind, use your breath. You don't need to take a drug.

Even if it's helpful to call a friend or seek a therapist's advice, these supportive people may not be available at 2:00 a.m. No matter what, you always have your breath.

8. Practice holding each of the yoga mudras as you read through the accompanying affirmations. Breathe along as you hold each mudra and repeat the positive thoughts in your mind. By spending time moving through all the mudras and reciting the positive mantras, notice how you can uplift yourself all the way down to the soul level.
9. Explore your unique vibration as you breathe into your energy body -- your pranamaya kosha. Your energy signature is as unique as your fingerprint. Enjoy the bliss of experiencing yourself unencumbered by excessive mind chatter. Bring yourself into the present moment and enjoy being you!

About The Photographer

A mother to three and grandmother to seven, Diane Fulmer discovered her passion for photography after retiring from a career in nursing.

You can see more of her excellent photograpy at www.dianebookerphotography.com.

"My hope is that my photographs will evoke some emotion and a wish to linger," Diane says.

Diane Fulmer returned to Armstrong Atlantic State University in Savannah to learn the deeper aspects of image making, with a strong love for printing from the negative in a digital world. Diane immersed herself in classical black and white and lith printing, a darkroom process used widely in Europe. She continues to explore new techniques including the art of digital photography.

Although Diane prefers coastal scenes, she also enjoys architecture, still life and portraits captured in the landscape. She strives to bring emotion and meaning to her photographs and uses SLR and medium format film and digital cameras.

Her nursing background and desire to share her passion led her to volunteer at Hospice Savannah as photographer for End of Life Family Photographer, a program she started in 2007.

Diane continues to develop her darkroom skills through independent studies at AASU and demonstrate her Lith and Sepia techniques for Photography classes at AASU under Linda Jensen, Professor of Photography. In March 2010, she attended a seven-day workshop with John Sexton in Carmel, California, to refine her photography and darkroom skills.

About The Author, Catherine Carrigan

Catherine Carrigan is a medical intuitive healer and Amazon No. 1 bestselling author. She has taught yoga for 24 years and empowers her clients to alleviate pain and suffering through a wide range of natural healing methods.

You can connect with her on Facebook at https://www.facebook.com/catherinecarriganauthor

Follow her on Twitter at
https://twitter.com/CSCarrigan

Read her blog at www.catherinecarrigan.com

Check out her websites at
www.catherinecarrigan.com and
www.unlimitedenergynow.com

Connect with her on LinkedIn at:
www.linkedin.com/in/catherinecarrigan/

Keep up with news about her books at:
https://www.goodreads.com/author/show/638831.Catherine_Carrigan

Sign up for her newsletter at:
http://bit.ly/1C4CFOC

You can read testimonials from her clients here:
http://catherinecarrigan.com/testimonials/

Training in Fitness

- Certified Personal Fitness Trainer: A.C.E. certified in Personal Fitness Training
- Corrective High-Performance Exercise Kinesiologist (C.H.E.K) Practitioner, Level I: C.H.E.K. Institute.
- Certified Group Exercise Instructor: A.C.E. certified in Group Exercise
- A.C.E. Specialty Recognitions: Strength Training and Mind-Body Fitness
- Exercise Coach, C.H.E.K. Institute
- Certified Yoga Teacher: 500-hour Yoga Teacher through Lighten Up Yoga; six 200-hour certifications through Integrative Yoga Therapy, the White Lotus Foundation, and the Atlanta Yoga Fellowship, Lighten Up Yoga and Erich Schiffmann teacher training (twice)

- Practitioner of qi gong, Chinese martial arts
- Certified Older Adult Fitness Trainer through the American Institute of Fitness Educators

Training in Nutrition

- Food Healing Level II Facilitator
- Holistic Lifestyle Coach though the C.H.E.K. Institute, Level 3
- Certified Sports Nutritionist through the American Aerobics Association International/International Sports Medicine Association
- Author, *Healing Depression: A Holistic Guide* (New York: Marlowe and Co., 1999), a book discussing nutrition and lifestyle to heal depression without drugs
- Schwarzbein Practitioner though Dr. Diana Schwarzbein, an expert in balancing hormones naturally

Training in Healing

- Specialized Kinesiology and Life Coaching through Sue Maes of London, Ontario, Canada

- Self-Empowerment Technology Practitioner
- Brain Gym, Vision Circles and Brain Organization instructor through the Educational Kinesiology Foundation
- Certified Touch for Health Practitioner
- Thai Yoga Body Therapy
- Flower Essence Practitioner
- Reiki Master, Usui Tradition
- Life Coaching through Sue Maes' Mastering Your Knowledge Mentorship Program and Peak Potentials
- Therapeutic Energy Kinesiology (TEK)
- Medical Intuitive Readings and Quantum Healing

Other Training

- Health and fitness columnist
- Playwright of 12 plays, including three produced in New York City
- Past spokesperson for the Depression Wellness Network
- Phi Beta Kappa graduate of Brown University
- Former national spokesperson for Johnson & Johnson
- Owner and co-host, Total Fitness Radio Show

- Author of *Healing Depression: A Holistic Guide*
- Author of the Amazon No. 1 best seller *What Is Healing? Awaken Your Intuitive Power for Health and Happiness*
- Author of the Amazon No. 1 best seller, *Unlimited Energy Now*
- Author of the Amazon No. 1 best seller, *Banish the Blues Now*
- Author of *What Is Social Media Today? Get Ready to Win the Game of Social Media*
- Author of the Amazon No. 1 best seller, *What Is Social Media Today? Hashtags, Keywords and You, Oh My!*
- Author of the Amazon No. 1 best seller, *The Difference Between Pain and Suffering*

About the Cover Design

This photograph of a purple lotus was taken at Brookgreen Gardens in South Carolina by the author Catherine Carrigan.

Beautiful lotus flowers grow out of the mud.

In the same way, our souls grow into the light out of the darkness of our own personal experiences.

THE DIFFERENCE
between
PAIN and SUFFERING

CATHERINE CARRIGAN

- Overcome your pain and suffering the natural way.
- Medical intuitive healer Catherine Carrigan shows you how.
- Discover drug-free secrets from yoga, Reiki, the world's
- Healthiest foods, energy healing and holistic alternative medicine
- With photographs and exercises that really work.

What is
HEALING?
AMAZON
#1
BESTSELLER
Awaken Your
Intuitive Power for
Health and Happiness
CATHERINE
CARRIGAN

About *What Is Healing? Awaken Your Intuitive Power for Health and Happiness*

In this book, you will:

- Learn how unconditional love can awaken your intuitive gifts.
- Reveal how to open your heart to access your highest intelligence.
- Uncover how to communicate with your angels and spiritual guides.
- Awaken your own psychic abilities.
- Identify the key aspects of a medical intuitive reading.
- Discern how addiction to staying sick can keep you from healing.
- Reveal the blessing behind a mental or physical breakdown.
- Grasp the four key difficulties that lead to health problems.
- Empower your own spiritual growth.

UNLIMITED
ENERGY
NOW
AMAZON
#1
BESTSELLER
CATHERINE
CARRIGAN

About *Unlimited Energy Now*

Discover the secrets of how you can experience unlimited energy *now:*

- Learn how to operate your body at its very best.
- Master your own energy system.
- Resolve the emotions that drain you.
- Connect to your highest intelligence.
- Inspire yourself to connect more deeply to your infinite, eternal and unwavering support from your soul.

Banish the Blues
NOW
Catherine Carrigan

Banish the Blues NOW addresses:

HEALING DEPRESSION WITHOUT DRUGS using NATURAL HEALING remedies. Did you know that the Centers for Disease Control and Prevention reports that **11 percent of all Americans over the age of 12 take antidepressants**?

Women are more likely than men to take these drugs at every level of severity of depression.

Non-Hispanic white persons are more likely to take antidepressants than are non-Hispanic black and Mexican-American persons.

Of those **taking antidepressants, 60 percent have taken them for more than 2 years, and 14 percent have taken the drugs for more than 10 years.** About 8 percent of persons aged 12 and over with no current depressive symptoms took antidepressant medication.

Despite the widespread acceptance of natural healing methods, from 1988-1994 through 2005-2008, the rate of antidepressant use in the United States among all ages increased nearly 400 percent.

It is my prayer that my new book will be of service in teaching you how to heal depression without drugs, banishing your
blues FOR GOOD!

FOREWARD By Abram Hoffer, M.D., Ph.D., FRCP(C) Editor, *The Journal of Orthomolecular Medicine*

Unlimited Intuition
NOW
AMAZON
#1
BESTSELLER
Catherine Carrigan

READ *UNLIMITEDINTUITION NOW*
TO DEVELOP YOUR OWN PSYCHIC ABILITIES SO THAT YOU CAN RECEIVE GUIDANCE FROM YOUR SOUL.

How you will benefit:

- Pray to open your soul guidance.
- Learn how to read the energy in your. chakras with a pendulum
- Tune in to read your own body.
- Discover how to read the body of another person.
- Discern how much life force is in your food.
- Focus to tell if food is really good for your body.
- Practice how to muscle test yourself.
- Raise your vibration to listen to your angels.
- Get your ego out of the way so you can listen to divine guidance.
- Stay connected with loved ones when you are apart.
- Open your psychic centers of clairaudience, claircognizance, clairsentience and clairvoyance.
- Avoid other people's ego projections to see what's really going on.
- Protect your energy so you feel safe and grounded at all times and in all places.
- Stay out of trouble in dangerous situations.
- Understand how your different psychic gifts actually work.
- Deepen your connection to God and feel supported on all level

What is Social Media TODAY

Get Ready to Win
The Game of Social Media

Catherine Carrigan

What is Social Media Today
Where Social Media is Fun

Lose your fear of social media

Tackle Twitter

Make friends with Facebook

Become a Youtube superstar

Create compelling viral content

Grow and brand your business

Hit page one of Google

Build your audience

Increase your income

Develop raving fans

What is
Social Media Today
Hashtags, Keywords And You
Oh My!

Catherine Carrigan

Are you making mistakes that keep you broke, without customers, readers or the success you deserve?

Keywords and Hashtags are the foundation for successful social media marketing.

What is Social Media Today is a broad based social media marketing training program.

You will have a consistent social media presence and will be posting like an expert in no time.

Read this book to learn how to use keywords and hashtags to build your tribe online and draw more customers for your products, books, services and business.

Made in the USA
San Bernardino, CA
09 September 2019